ENCORE

Encore

Original Stories by

W. SOMERSET MAUGHAM

Screenplays by

T. E. B. CLARKE

ARTHUR MACRAE

ERIC AMBLER

Doubleday & Company, Inc.

GARDEN CITY, NEW YORK, 1952

Library of Congress Catalog Card Number 52-8052

COPYRIGHT, 1924, 1935, 1943, 1952, BY W. SOMERSET MAUGHAM
ALL RIGHTS RESERVED
PRINTED IN THE UNITED STATES
AT
THE COUNTRY LIFE PRESS, GARDEN CITY, N.Y.
FIRST EDITION

CONTENTS

ENCORE

THE ANT AND THE GRASSHOPPER

WHEN I was a very small boy I was made to learn by heart certain of the fables of La Fontaine, and the moral of each was carefully explained to me. Among those I learnt was "The Ant and the Grasshopper," which is devised to bring home to the young the useful lesson that in an imperfect world industry is rewarded and giddiness punished. In this admirable fable (I apologize for telling something which everyone is politely, but inexactly, supposed to know) the ant spends a laborious summer gathering its winter store, while the grasshopper sits on a blade of grass singing to the sun. Winter comes and the ant is comfortably provided for, but the grasshopper has an empty larder: he goes to the ant and begs for a little food. Then the ant gives him her classic answer:

"What were you doing in the summertime?"

"Saving your presence, I sang, I sang all day, all night."

"You sang. Why, then go and dance."

I do not ascribe it to perversity on my part, but rather to the inconsequence of childhood, which is deficient in moral sense, that I could never quite reconcile myself to the lesson. My sympathies were with the grasshopper, and for some time I never saw an ant without putting my foot on it. In this summary (and, as I have discovered since, entirely human) fashion I sought to express my disapproval of prudence and common sense.

I could not help thinking of this fable when the other day I saw George Ramsay lunching by himself in a restaurant. I never saw anyone wear an expression of such deep gloom. He was staring into space. He looked as though the burden of the whole world sat on his shoulders. I was sorry for him: I suspected at once that his unfortunate brother had been causing trouble again. I went up to him and held out my hand.

"How are you?" I asked.

"I'm not in hilarious spirits."

"Is it Tom again?"

He sighed.

"Yes, it's Tom again."

"Why don't you chuck him? You've done everything in the world for him. You must know by now that he's quite hopeless."

I suppose every family has a black sheep. Tom had been a sore trial to his for twenty years. He had begun life decently enough: he went into business, married and had two children. The Ramsays were perfectly respectable people and there was every reason to suppose that Tom Ramsay would have a useful and honourable career. But one day, without warning, he announced that he didn't like work and that he wasn't suited for marriage. He wanted to enjoy himself. He would listen to no expostulations. He left his wife and his office. He had a little money and he spent two happy years in the various capitals of Europe. Rumours of his doings reached his relations from time to time and they were profoundly shocked. He certainly had a very good time. They shook their heads and asked what would happen when his money was spent. They soon found out: he borrowed. He was charming and unscrupulous. I have never met anyone to whom it was more difficult to refuse a loan. He made a steady income from his friends and he made friends easily. But he always said that the money you spent on necessities was boring; the money that was amusing to spend was the money you spent in luxuries. For this he depended on his brother George. He did not waste his charm on him. George was a serious man and insensible to such enticements. George was respectable. Once or twice he fell to Tom's promises of amendment and gave him considerable sums in order that he might make a fresh start. On these Tom bought a motorcar and some very nice jewelry. But when circumstances forced George to realize that his brother would never settle down and he washed his hands of him, Tom, without a qualm, began to blackmail him. It was not very nice for a respectable lawyer to find his brother shaking cocktails behind the bar of his favourite restaurant or to see him waiting on the box seat of a taxi outside his club. Tom said that to serve in a bar or to drive a taxi was a perfectly decent occupation, but if George could oblige him with a couple of hundred pounds he didn't mind, for the honour of the family, giving it up. George paid.

Once Tom nearly went to prison. George was terribly upset. He went into the whole discreditable affair. Really Tom had gone too far. He had been wild, thoughtless and selfish, but he had never before done anything dishonest, by which George meant illegal; and if he were prosecuted he would assuredly be convicted. But you cannot allow your only brother to go to gaol. The man Tom had cheated, a man called

Cronshaw, was vindictive. He was determined to take the matter into court; he said Tom was a scoundrel and should be punished. It cost George an infinite deal of trouble and five hundred pounds to settle the affair. I have never seen him in such a rage as when he heard that Tom and Cronshaw had gone off together to Monte Carlo the moment they cashed the cheque. They spent a happy month there.

For twenty years Tom raced and gambled, philandered with the prettiest girls, danced, ate in the most expensive restaurants, and dressed beautifully. He always looked as if he had just stepped out of a bandbox. Though he was forty-six you would never have taken him for more than thirty-five. He was a most amusing companion and though you knew he was perfectly worthless you could not but enjoy his society. He had high spirits, an unfailing gaiety and incredible charm. I never grudged the contributions he regularly levied on me for the necessities of his existence. I never lent him fifty pounds without feeling that I was in his debt. Tom Ramsay knew everyone and everyone knew Tom Ramsay. You could not approve of him, but you could not help liking him.

Poor George, only a year older than his scapegrace brother, looked sixty. He had never taken more than a fortnight's holiday in the year for a quarter of a century. He was in his office every morning at nine-thirty and never left it till six. He was honest, industrious and worthy. He had a good wife, to whom he had never been unfaithful even in thought, and four daughters to whom he was the best of fathers. He made a point of saving a third of his income, and his plan was to retire at fifty-five to a little house in the country where he proposed to cultivate his garden and play golf. His life was blameless. He was glad that he was growing old because Tom was growing old too. He rubbed his hands and said:

"It was all very well when Tom was young and good-looking, but he's only a year younger than I am. In four years he'll be fifty. He won't find life so easy then. I shall have thirty thousand pounds by the time I'm fifty. For twenty-five years I've said that Tom would end in the gutter. And we shall see how he likes that. We shall see if it really pays best to work or be idle."

Poor George! I sympathized with him. I wondered now as I sat down beside him what infamous thing Tom had done. George was evidently very much upset.

"Do you know what's happened now?" he asked me.

I was prepared for the worst. I wondered if Tom had got into the hands of the police at last. George could hardly bring himself to speak.

"You're not going to deny that all my life I've been hard-working, decent, respectable and straightforward. After a life of industry and thrift I can look forward to retiring on a small income in gilt-edged securities. I've always done my duty in that state of life in which it has pleased Providence to place me."

"True."

"And you can't deny that Tom has been an idle, worthless, dissolute and dishonourable rogue. If there were any justice he'd be in the workhouse."

"True."

George grew red in the face.

"A few weeks ago he became engaged to a woman old enough to be his mother. And now she's died and left him everything she had. Half a million pounds, a yacht, a house in London and a house in the country."

George Ramsay beat his clenched fist on the table.

"It's not fair, I tell you, it's not fair. Damn it, it's not fair."

I could not help it. I burst into a shout of laughter as I looked at George's wrathful face, I rolled in my chair, I very nearly fell on the floor. George never forgave me. But Tom often asks me to excellent dinners in his charming house in Mayfair and if he occasionally borrows a trifle from me that is merely force of habit. It is never more than a sovereign.

THE ANT AND THE GRASSHOPPER

List of Cast

Character	Artiste
TOM RAMSAY	NIGEL PATRICK
GEORGE RAMSAY	ROLAND CULVER
MR. BATEMAN	CHARLES VICTOR
FREDA RAMSAY	ALISON LEGGATT
MRS. BATEMAN	MARGARET WITHERS
PHILIP CRONSHAW	PETER GRAVES
MISS FARROW	DOROTHY BRAMHALL
SALLY	
(Reception Office)	PATRICIA RAINE
GERTRUDE WILMOT	MARGARET VYNER
PAWNBROKER	FRANK TICKLE
BOWLER-HATTED CLUBMAN	CAMPBELL COTTS
BRUNETTE	NAOMI CHANCE
OTHER MAN	MICHAEL TRUBSHAWE
MAID	PATRICIA GLYN

After the main credit titles, DISSOLVE *to a series of shots of Somerset Maugham in his garden, under which there is the following narration:*

"No novel, or play, or short story written by Somerset Maugham could ever be mistaken for the work of another writer, they are characteristically his. So now that we have made three more of his stories into a film it seems suitable

15

to take our camera to the South of France where he lives, and ask him to introduce them to you."

Mr. Maugham has, by now, got fairly near the camera and sits by a small garden table:

MR. MAUGHAM: Ladies and gentlemen, I am really quite ashamed to face you again. You will begin to think I fancy myself as a film actor, but I assure you that I don't. It is because I don't that I am talking to you from my garden. I thought that if you were tired of looking at me you could look at the flowers. Today you're going to see three more of my stories arranged for the screen by three very clever script writers. The stories are founded on fact, but of course they are fiction, and like every other author I have looked upon it as my right to arrange my facts to suit my purpose, which was to entertain.

1. MR. MAUGHAM: The aim of "The Ant and The Grass-hopper" is to amuse. You must not look in it for a moral because there isn't one. My hero was a very lucky man; he is just the exception which proves the rule that, on the whole, honesty is the best policy and, in this hard world, if you want to eat you must work.

DISSOLVE To

2. *Insert. Book open at story. The Narrator reads the first line.*

NARRATOR: I suppose every family has a black sheep. Tom Ramsay was a sore trial to his.

DISSOLVE To

3. *Exterior Pawnbroker's Shop. Day. Close shot. Door of the shop. As Tom Ramsay comes out of the shop, the Narrator makes his final comment.*

NARRATOR: He had long ago announced that he didn't like work; he wanted to enjoy himself.

Tom closes the door of the shop and, as his arm drops from the doorknob, we . . .

CUT To

4. *Tom, standing outside the shop. He fumbles for his cigarette case over his hip pocket. At once he recalls its recent sad fate and takes a loose cigarette from his breast*

pocket. He fumbles for his lighter, but this, of course, has gone the way of the cigarette case. He stands for a moment undecided, then, with a nonchalant shrug of his shoulders, turns back into the shop.

5. *Interior Pawnbroker's Shop. Day. Tom Ramsay walks from the door up to the counter, the stooping figure of the Pawnbroker standing into right foreground of screen. Tom comes up to the counter and, turning on the never-failing charm, says:*

TOM: Would you let me use my lighter once more?

6. *Interior Pawnbroker's Shop. Day. Reverse over shoulder of pawnbroker. He looks at Tom for a moment with a dead-pan face and then, as though conferring a great favour, reaches under the counter, brings out the lighter, flicks it and offers it to Tom.*

TOM (*with great dignity*): Very kind of you, thanks.
With a facetious wave, he turns on his heel and walks away to the door.

DISSOLVE To

7. *Interior Reception Office. Day. Close Shot. Black letters on frosted panel of door:*

BLAIR AND RAMSAY
SOLICITORS AND COMMISSIONERS FOR OATHS

CUT To

8. *Interior Reception Office. Day. Sally at switchboard left foreground. Reception door right background. Tom enters, just a trifle gingerly, then, rapidly gaining confidence, strides up to Sally.*

TOM: Hullo, Sally.
SALLY: Oh, hullo, Mr. Tom.
TOM: Yes, well, er, do you think I could see my brother for a minute?
SALLY (*not very hopeful*): Well, I'll see if he's in.
She plugs into the switchboard and twiddles the handle.

9. *Interior George's office. Day. George answers his phone.*
GEORGE: Yes. (*Looking grim*) Oh, is he? Keep him out there. I'll send Miss Farrow.

Miss Farrow is already rising as George puts down the phone.

GEORGE: I'm afraid it's my brother again. I don't want to see him.

MISS FARROW (*with an understanding nod*): Quite.

GEORGE: Get rid of him.

MISS FARROW: I will, Mr. Ramsay.

Miss Farrow exits.

10. *Interior Reception Office. Day. Medium shot of Miss Farrow closing George's office door behind her. She moves upstage as she says her line.*

MISS FARROW (*coldly*): I'm afraid Mr. Ramsay is busy.

11. *Interior Reception Office. Day.*

TOM: Hullo, Patricia. I say, you've got a new hair-do! Suits you.

By this time he is peering around the back of her head.

TOM: Yes, I like it.

MISS FARROW (*turning on him*): I said Mr. Ramsay is far too busy to see you.

TOM: Trade booming, is it? Splendid. That's all right . . .

He sits on the sofa.

TOM: I can wait.

He puts his feet up.

TOM: I've got all the time in the world.

12. *Interior Reception Office. Day. Medium close shot of Miss Farrow. She is beginning to lose some of her assurance.*

MISS FARROW: Mr. Ramsay, you can't lie down there.

13. *Interior Reception Office. Day.*

TOM: Yes, really, it's perfectly comfortable. Don't you worry about me.

Miss Farrow, getting flustered, steps up towards the couch and looks down at Tom.

MISS FARROW: Mr. Ramsay . . . (*with a note of appeal*) . . . please.

14. *Interior Reception Office. Day.*

TOM (*opening one eye*): Of course, if you could spare a cup of tea when the trolley comes round . . .

15. *Interior George's Office. Day. Miss Farrow, like a flustered hen, returns to George's office.*

MISS FARROW: Mr. Ramsay, I'm sorry . . . but he insists on waiting.

16. *Interior George's Office. Day.*

GEORGE (*uninterested*): Well, let him wait. He'll soon get bored. Now then, where were we?

MISS FARROW: But he's lying down on the couch.

GEORGE (*reacting with alarm*): Is he drunk?

MISS FARROW: No, he's quite sober, I think.

GEORGE (*clucking with annoyance. Then he looks extremely anxious*): Oh dear . . . we have Sir James Fawcett due in ten minutes. This is intolerable.

George gets up from his desk and starts to pace up and down for a few seconds.

GEORGE: I shall have to see him . . . if only to get rid of him. You'd better show him in.

MISS FARROW (*off*): Very well, Mr. Ramsay.

GEORGE: Oh, Miss Farrow, while you're waiting you might check those accounts. There's sevenpence to be deducted from Loveday and Wheeler's. My wife paid cash for the item I've marked.

As Miss Farrow exits . . .

CUT TO

17. *Interior Reception Office. Day. Close shot of Tom as he gets up from couch.*

TOM: Hello, George, you're looking a bit peaky.

CUT TO

18. *Interior George's Office. Day. Tom smiles at Miss Farrow as he passes her and walks into George's office.*

TOM: Not overdoing it, I hope.

GEORGE: I haven't much time, Tom.

TOM (*passing George and entering office*): This won't take a minute.

GEORGE: And I've certainly no money to spare.

TOM (*brought to a stop and turning to face George*): Oh . . . (*He faces into the room again.*) I'm afraid it's going to take a bit longer.

GEORGE: I made it quite plain when you were last here

19

that you'd never get another penny out of me, and I'm a man of my word.

George now begins to walk towards his desk. Tom saunters after him, a pace or two behind.

TOM: I know you are, George. Also you're hard-working, decent, respectable and straightforward. . . . That is the usual order, isn't it?

GEORGE (*stung*): There's no need for sarcasm. (*He turns and faces Tom, doing his best to look haughty and scornful. This results in making Tom even more infuriatingly flippant.*)

TOM: And you cannot see what you've done to be saddled with a brother who's—what are the exact words?

GEORGE (*sitting after line*): Idle, worthless and dissolute.

TOM (*nodding*): That's it . . . Oh, and a disgrace to an old and honourable family.

He flops into a chair opposite George with as much nonchalance and informality as possible.

TOM (*continuing*): Well, now we've got that over, let's get down to business. What I really need is a couple of hundred pounds, but . . .

19. *Interior George's Office. Day.*

GEORGE: Not another penny.

TOM: I was going to say, I don't want to be unreasonable. I could scrape through on a hundred and fifty.

GEORGE: I'm not interested. If you can't scrape through on what you've got . . .

20. *Interior George's Office. Day.*

TOM (*gets out of his chair with great deliberation, fumbling in his pockets for loose change*): My dear George, that is precisely one pound, eight shillings and fourpence.

He turns his back on George and moves downstage.

GEORGE: What's the matter with getting yourself a job?

TOM (*turning leisurely, looks at George for a moment before speaking*): Really, George, that one-track mind of yours! Do you realize you've been sitting in that same chair repeating yourself with unfailing regularity for the last fifteen years?

Tom has walked back and sits on the arm of the heavy, pompous leather chair.

GEORGE: It's a pity you didn't listen to me before. Fifteen years ago, when you were young and fresh-looking . . . well, you might have landed (*this a most grudging admission*) something good.

21. *Interior George's Office. Day. George is now warming to his subject and feels he is speaking really quite well and most reasonably.*

GEORGE: Now . . . what are you? Eighteen months between us . . . you'll soon be forty. Good jobs aren't so easy to come by when a man's middle-aged. You'll find that out.

At this point Tom indolently flops into the chair, his legs dangling over the arm. A character less likely to do a hard day's work it would be hard to imagine. On the above action . . .

CUT TO

22. *Interior George's Office. Day. Close shot of Tom.*

TOM: Exactly, so you must agree, then, that I'll need something to tide me over while I'm looking for one.

23. *Interior George's Office. Day. Close shot of George.*

GEORGE: Not—one—more—penny!

He glowers at Tom. Tom smiles back at him, then, with a slight shrug of his shoulders, he gets out of the chair.

TOM: Well, of course, if you want your only brother to end in the gutter . . .

GEORGE: It's where I've always said you'd end!

TOM (*standing at the corner of the desk and looking down at George*): Yes, and you always love to be right, don't you, George?

GEORGE: We'll see whether it really pays to work or be idle.

TOM (*almost at the door*): To the gutter.

GEORGE: We'll see how you like it.

The phone rings and George immediately answers it. Tom hovers at the door for a few seconds and then, with a jaunty wave, leaves.

GEORGE (*into phone*): Yes . . . Oh, good afternoon, Mr. Bateman . . . (*Tom exits. As phone rings returns to pick up £1.8.4d.*) Now what do you want? . . . Not you, my

21

dear chap (*into phone*). (*Tom exits.*) Thursday lunch? At the club? Yes, I'm free. Splendid.

DISSOLVE TO

24. *Exterior West End Club. Day.* (*Location.*) *George and Bateman leaving lobby of club and walking down steps towards camera.*

BATEMAN: It sounds the sort of place we're looking for. I'll talk it over with my wife.

GEORGE: Perhaps you'll both dine with me one night?

BATEMAN: We'd be delighted.

GEORGE: Do you know Rinaldi's?

BATEMAN: Indeed I do.

GEORGE (*to the doorman off scene*): Oh, doorman.

25. *Exterior West End Club. Day.* (*Location.*) *Close shot, Tom turning into camera.*

TOM: Yes, sir.

26. *Exterior West End Club. Day.* (*Location.*) *Close shot, George reacting.*

GEORGE: Call us . . . a . . . taxi . . . will you?

27. *Exterior West End Club. Day.* (*Location.*) *Tom looks off camera left, raises his hand, puts two fingers into his mouth and gives out a piercing whistle. Bateman goes on talking, unaware of the shock George has had. Tom spots a taxi and moves forward out of shot.*

BATEMAN: As places go these days, it takes a lot of beating. I didn't know it was a haunt of yours. Go there much?

GEORGE (*dithering*): Er . . . er, what did you say?

BATEMAN (*surprised*): Rinaldi's.

GEORGE (*trying to pull himself together*): Oh yes—yes, I know it well. My favourite restaurant.

Bateman gives George a puzzled look and then looks off left.

28. *Exterior West End Club. Day.* (*Location.*) *Taxi pulling up at curb. Tom immediately opens the door. As he does so, cut on action.*

29. *Exterior West End Club. Day.* (*Location.*) *Bateman gestures to George to precede him.*

22

BATEMAN: After you.

GEORGE: No, I—I think on second thoughts I'll walk. I don't really get enough exercise.

BATEMAN: Sure? Well, I'll wait till I hear from you.

He moves forward to the cab, is about to get inside, when he fumbles for change, brings out a bob and hands it to Tom.

30. *Exterior West End Club. Day. (Location.) Close shot of George. As, off scene, he hears Tom say: "Thank you, sir," he reacts as though he has received a sharp blow in the mid-section. He hears the door slam, does his poor best to squeeze a faint smile onto his face as the taxi drives off. Tom steps back onto the pavement.*

GEORGE: What the devil do you mean by this?

TOM (*his arms folded in front of him, looks straight ahead, like a sentry on duty*): You told me to get myself a job. Well, I took your advice.

GEORGE: It was a shameful thing to do.

Between their two heads a bowler-hatted figure is seen walking down the steps towards them.

TOM: What's shameful about being a doorman? It's a perfectly respectable occupation. But, if you'll oblige me with a couple of hundred quid, I don't mind, for the honour of the family . . .

GEORGE: I won't do it.

Tom, with great patience, as though dealing with a spoilt child, turns with a sigh to look at George.

31. *Exterior West End Club. Day. (Location.) Close shot, of bowler-hatted member. He is walking to camera and suddenly stops as though struck dead by what he has heard.*

TOM (*off*): Now, look, George, you can't have it both ways.

32. *Exterior West End Club. Day. (Location.) George reacts guiltily to the old member and, in a hurried whisper, says:*

GEORGE: Come to the office.

He exits and Tom turns towards the old member.

TOM (*saluting*): Taxi, sir?

OLD MEMBER (*off*): Yes.

33. *Insert. Signature of George Ramsay being written on cheque.*

34. *Interior George's Office. Day. George blots cheque and tears it out of his book. Handing it to Tom, he looks up at him.*

GEORGE: It is to be clearly understood that you find something suitable to your station in life.

35. *Interior George's Office. Day. Close shot of Tom. He gets up as he says his line.*

TOM: All right, don't worry. I'll confine my activities to the highest possible circles.

DISSOLVE To

36. *Exterior Ascot Racecourse. Day. (Stock.) A library shot of the field in the Ascot Gold Cup, sweeping round the final bend into the straight. (Superimpose field-glass roundlets over the shot.)*

37. *Exterior Royal Enclosure. Ascot. Day. Close shot of Tom, just recognizable in spite of field glasses to his eyes and Ascot-grey topper.*

TOM: It's all right, darling—in the bag! Minorca's walking it. Money for jam! . . . only class horse in the race.

38. *Exterior Enclosure. Ascot. Day. Close shot of beautiful brunette. Very calm.*

BRUNETTE: Is that Minorca going into the lead now?

TOM: What? (*Looking hastily through glasses.*)

39. *Exterior Royal Enclosure. Ascot. Day. Three shot of brunette, Tom and another man, who now starts shouting.*

OTHER MAN: What price Beamish Boy! Beamish Boy's got it! Beamish is walking it! RIDE HIM, JOHNNY!

TOM (*anxious*): Get up there, Minorca—get . . . up!

OTHER MAN: Beamish Boy wins.

40. *Exterior Royal Enclosure. Ascot. Day. Individual of other man. He turns to Tom.*

OTHER MAN: There's class for you, sir.

41. *Interior Rinaldi's Cocktail Bar. Night. George and Bateman are approaching the bar.*

GEORGE: Of course, that's another great advantage about the place—the train service is excellent. Now, what are you going to have?

(*At this moment the back of a white-coated figure walks into shot and we notice George's startled reaction.*)

42. *Interior Rinaldi's Cocktail Bar. Night. Close shot of Tom.*

TOM: Good evening, gentlemen.

BATEMAN: New chap, this.

GEORGE (*thoroughly shaken*): Yes, yes, I think he is . . . Er, what'll have you have?

BATEMAN: Pink gin for me.

TOM: What can I get you, sir?

43. *Interior Rinaldi's Cocktail Bar. Night. George is scowling at Tom.*

GEORGE: Two pink gins.

TOM (*most deferential and courteous*): Two pink gins, large?

George has no alternative but to nod angrily. Tom turns into camera and exits from shot, leaving George looking after him, puzzled.

BATEMAN: His face seems very familiar.

GEORGE (*wretchedly*): It does.

BATEMAN (*leaning over the bar and addressing Tom*): What's your name?

TOM (*off*): Tom, sir.

George winces.

BATEMAN: You ever served me before anywhere?

44. *Interior Rinaldi's Cocktail Bar. Night.*

TOM: I think I've seen you, sir. Don't you sometimes go to the Merry Hell Club?

45. *Interior Rinaldi's Cocktail Bar. Night.*

BATEMAN: I do not.

At this moment we hear off screen Bateman's name being paged. As he turns towards boy shouting from door . . .

Two shot of George and Bateman at the bar.

BATEMAN (*reacting to pageboy, climbs off his stool and exits shot*): Ah, that'll be Margaret. All right, boy.

GEORGE (*leaning forward*): You double-crossing cad.

46. *Interior Rinaldi's Cocktail Bar. Night.*

TOM: Not at all. I assured you I'd mix only with the smartest people.

47. *Interior Rinaldi's Cocktail Bar. Night.*

GEORGE: Well, it's not going to work again. I'm very fond of this place, but sooner than be blackmailed any more, I'll cut it right out of my life.

48. *Interior Rinaldi's Cocktail Bar. Night. Shot over George's shoulder, of Tom bringing drinks to bar.*

TOM (*smiling*): That'll be eight shillings, sir, if you please.

49. *Interior Rinaldi's Cocktail Bar. Night. Group shot, from behind the bar. In background, Bateman and wife are seen walking through door and up to bar. George slaps down a pound note. George reacts to Bateman's remark as he approaches and climbs off his stool.*

BATEMAN: Here we are, my dear, let me introduce Mr. Ramsay.

GEORGE (*taking a step or two downstage*): How do you do, Mrs. Bateman.

MRS. BATEMAN: Stephen has often spoken of you.

GEORGE (*smiling politely*): Well, I hope?

BATEMAN: You wait till we start doing business together.

There is a ripple of well-mannered laughter.

GEORGE: What would you like to drink, Mrs. Bateman?

MRS. BATEMAN: Nothing at the moment, thank you.

TOM (*walking back into shot and addressing George*): Your change, sir.

GEORGE (*to Batemans*): Excuse me.

He moves back to the bar as Tom puts down a ten-shilling note and a florin. George picks up the note and the florin, hesitates, then reluctantly pushes the coin across the bar.

50. *Interior Rinaldi's Cocktail Bar. Night.*
   TOM (*delighted with his tip*): Thank you very much indeed, sir.

51. *Interior George's Office. Day. Wide angle two shot, windows in background. George and Bateman, right and left of screen, are leaning over desk peering at photographs. George's chair is moved out of the way, but just in shot.*
   GEORGE: My father had this room added on just after the turn of the century.
   From below, outside the window, a loud whistling starts, followed almost immediately by the top of a ladder, which waves about for a bit and then comes to rest as it is leant above the window. The two at the desk react to the ladder, but take no immediate notice of it.
   BATEMAN: Is it big enough for a billiard table?
   GEORGE: Yes, that was the reason. Of course, billiards was all the rage about that time.
   The whistling becomes annoyingly loud. George reacts again and starts to walk towards the window.

52. *Interior George's Office. Day.*
   GEORGE: I don't play the game myself, so . . .
   BATEMAN: Oh, I like billiards.
   GEORGE (*pleased*): Well, then.
   He is now in foreground and, as he turns towards the window, he looks stern.
   GEORGE: Hey, you outside there, stop that . . . filthy . . .

53. *Interior George's Office. Day. Close individual shot. Tom's head and shoulders appearing above window ledge.*
   GEORGE (*off*): . . . racket . . .
   TOM: Beg pardon, sir.
   George, rooted to the same spot, has his eyes closed in hopeless resignation. Then he looks at Tom and, on a minor note, says:
   GEORGE: Could you do your job more quietly?
   Tom smiling. He has a cloth cap perched rakishly over one ear and wears blue dungarees.
   TOM: Sure, sorry, guv.

54. *Interior George's Office. Day. George looks extremely worried after glancing at Bateman.*

55. *Interior George's Office. Day. Bateman. He is looking at Tom with that "Where have I seen him before?" expression. George, trying to become master of the situation, advances bracingly to the desk. He leans over and collects the photographs. He hands them to Bateman, at the same time placing himself so that he obstructs Bateman's view of Tom.*

GEORGE: Look, I tell you what, why don't you take these away with you and sort of get a mental picture of the layout?

BATEMAN (*surprised*): Yes, all right, I suppose you are rather busy.

He looks past George, or tries to, but has to take a side step to get a good look at Tom. He is thwarted in this as George bends over the desk to get a cigarette out of the silver box. He offers this to Bateman as he changes his position to obstruct the view once more.

BATEMAN: No, thanks, Ramsay, not now.

GEORGE (*handing Bateman the photographs*): Any time you'd like to come back and see the house . . .

BATEMAN (*taking the hint and moving towards the door*): Thanks, I'll give you a ring.

They take two or three steps towards the door and then Bateman stops and returns quickly to the desk as he says . . .

BATEMAN: Oh, my hat.

GEORGE: Here we are. Well, I'll look forward to hearing from you.

Once more the camera tracks with them to the door. George almost succeeds in getting rid of Bateman, but at the last moment he peers round George and addresses a remark to the window cleaner.

BATEMAN: Are you a Wimbledon window cleaner?

56. *Interior George's Office. Day. Close shot of Tom.*

TOM: Elephant and Castle's me regular beat, sir. Been promoted today.

57. *Interior George's Office. Day.*

BATEMAN: Hm, very odd . . . Well, so long, Ramsay.

Bateman disappears through the door and George gives an obvious sigh of relief. But he is not left in peace very long.

Tom (*breathing again on the window and polishing most conscientiously*): You're surely not selling Chartfield?

58. *Interior George's Office. Day.*

George: Mind your own business.

Tom: As you wish. (*Scratches windowpane with his little finger, then wets index finger with spit and again scratches with little finger.*) You know, it's rather a pleasant business, this. Not very aristocratic, of course, but healthy, invigorating.

George: This is not going to do you the slightest bit of good. You've had all you'll ever get out of me.

Tom: Don't tell me you're hard up, George.

George (*at first ignoring the remark, then turning to look at Tom. He is unable to conceal a note of anxiety in his voice*): Don't you start spreading rumours like that about me.

Tom (*quick to take advantage*): Well, why are you selling Chartfield? I thought you loved the place.

George (*still pacing in front of his desk*): It's got nothing whatever to do with . . . (*He leans back against the desk.*) On second thoughts, I will tell you; then, perhaps, you'll leave me alone in future.

Tom (*pushing the window open still further and stepping into the room*): This is all most intriguing.

As he advances into the room, we cut round to reverse. Tom saunters up to him and helps himself to a cigarette from George's box.

George: It so happens that John Blair has decided to retire this year. He has given me a chance to acquire full control of the firm and I have agreed to buy him out.

Tom lights up and blows out a cloud of smoke with great satisfaction.

George (*continuing*): I need all the money I can raise. I shouldn't be selling Chartfield if I had any more to waste on you. Now do you understand?

They look at each other for a second or two.

Tom: You're an extraordinary chap, George. Father

leaves you a lovely old place like Chartfield and you go and give it up for a sordid thing like a prosperous business.

GEORGE (*stung, begins to move round to his chair*): Rather less sordid, I should have thought, than begging and blackmailing.

59. *Interior George's Office. Day. Tom looks at George and smiles benignly at him.*

TOM: Not a bit. All the money I've got out of you has been put to the best possible use.

GEORGE (*flopping into chair*): Bah!

TOM: The pursuit of happiness.

GEORGE: Will you stop talking nonsense and go now. I've said all I had to say.

TOM: Are you happy, George? Do you get any fun at all out of life?

They both react and turn towards the door as they hear it opened.

60. *Interior George's Office. Day. Miss Farrow checks with a gasp as she sees her employer talking to a window cleaner whom she recognizes as his brother. She is about to withdraw when, off screen, we hear George's first line.*

GEORGE (*off*): All right, Miss Farrow.

61. *Interior George's Office. Day. Close shot of George. For once he is surprisingly cool and unembarrassed by his brother.*

GEORGE: Come in. Show Mr. Ramsay to the window.

He sits down, quite unaware that he has made a witty remark.

FADE OUT

FADE IN TO

62. *Exterior Chartfield Manor. Day. (Location.) Tracking shot down the driveway of George and Bateman. Their wives in background about ten yards behind. The men are just reaching the drive as the shot starts.*

BATEMAN: I tell you what . . . I'll make you a flat offer of seven and a half thousand. I don't believe in haggling.

GEORGE (*both start off down drive*): Neither do I. Let's split the difference and call it seven thousand seven fifty.

BATEMAN (*shaking his head*): It's too much, Ramsay. Seven thousand six hundred is my fixed limit.

GEORGE: I won't bargain, I never do. However, I don't mind knocking off the odd fifty. Seven thousand seven hundred.

They stop as they reach Bateman's car.

BATEMAN: Well, what's fifty pounds here or there? I'll meet you halfway . . . call it seven thousand six hundred and fifty.

GEORGE: Well, to save haggling—I'll meet you. Seven thousand six hundred and seventy-five . . .

As Bateman is thinking this over, we cut to . . .

63. *Exterior Chartfield Manor. Day. (Location.) Freda and Mrs. Bateman.*

FREDA: . . . if we say September the first?

MRS. BATEMAN: That should give us time enough.

Bateman and George are now in shot, just as they shake on the deal.

BATEMAN: O.K., Ramsay, it's a deal.

FREDA (*the two women joining the men*): Have you men finished your little business talk?

BATEMAN: Yes, we're through.

GEORGE: We aren't the sort to beat about the bush.

MRS. BATEMAN (*to Freda, shaking hands*): It's been so nice. Just like spending the day with friends.

FREDA: Come down whenever you like, don't bother to ask.

64. *Exterior Chartfield Manor. Day. (Location.)*

BATEMAN (*stepping forward to shake hands*): Thank you, Mrs. Ramsay. I hope you won't hate us too much for turning you out of your beautiful home.

65. *Exterior Chartfield Manor. Day. (Location.)*

FREDA: I'll try not to.

66. *Exterior Chartfield Manor. Day. (Location.)*

BATEMAN (*clambering into car*): So long, Ramsay, I'll instruct my solicitors. (*He bangs door, starts car and immediately drives off with a wave.*)

George and Freda move up into shot as they wave.

FREDA (*between waves*): Satisfactory?

GEORGE (*giving a final wave*): Yes, I worked him up quite a bit.

As they turn to walk towards the house, the camera dollies with them.

GEORGE: I'm going to miss the old place. (*He stops and looks at the house.*)

FREDA (*jockeying him along. They move on*): I'm not. If you had the running of this house . . . it's going to be heaven to get into a nice modern flat.

GEORGE: Anyway, it'll stop Tom using this address to impress his girl friends.

He chuckles.

FREDA: Don't mention that brother of yours to me! You really think you've seen the last of him?

GEORGE (*walking past camera*): It's over a month now . . . even Tom knows when to accept the inevitable.

They are just about to enter the house when they both become conscious (screen left) of a car approaching down the drive. They look towards the entrance gates.

GEORGE: Who on earth can this be?

As George moves back again to the top of the entrance steps and stands waiting for the car, we cut to a reverse angle.

67. *Exterior Chartfield Manor. Day. (Location.) A car approaches and stops opposite George.*

CRONSHAW (*hardly visible behind the windscreen*): Is this where Mr. Ramsay lives?

GEORGE: It is.

CRONSHAW (*switching off engine*): Ah!

68. *Exterior Chartfield Manor. Day. (Location.) Cronshaw looks up at George.*

CRONSHAW: Is he at home?

69. *Exterior Chartfield Manor. Day. (Location.) Close shot of George.*

GEORGE: I am Mr. Ramsay.

CRONSHAW (*taken aback*): Oh, it's Tom Ramsay I'm looking for.

GEORGE: My brother? He hasn't lived here for a long time.

CRONSHAW (*puzzled*): He hasn't?

GEORGE (*off*): Not since he was a boy.

CRONSHAW: But this was the address he gave me only last Thursday.

GEORGE: He had no right to.

CRONSHAW (*off*): Where can I find him?

GEORGE (*annoyed by his tone*): I haven't the least idea.

70. *Exterior Chartfield Manor. Day. (Location.) Close individual of Cronshaw.*

CRONSHAW (*looks at George suspiciously*): No? . . . That's a pity. Means I'll have to get the police on the job.

71. *Exterior Chartfield Manor. Day. (Location.) Close individual of George.*

GEORGE (*shocked*): The police?

CRONSHAW (*half apologetically*): Nothing else for it.

Cronshaw switches on the ignition and presses the self-starter.

GEORGE (*trying to preserve his presence of mind*): I feel sure this can all be explained.

CRONSHAW: I very much doubt it.

GEORGE: Can't we talk this over? How about a cup of tea?

CRONSHAW: No tea, thanks, but if it'll make you feel any better, I don't mind giving you details.

GEORGE (*off*): Thanks.

CRONSHAW (*switching off again*): Sorry if I've given you a shock. (*Starts to climb out of car.*)

On this action CUT TO

72. *Exterior Chartfield Manor. Day. (Location.) Two shot of Cronshaw and George. The camera dollies back to the terrace and pans them to tea table.*

CRONSHAW: By the way, my name's Cronshaw. Portland Motor Mart, secondhand cars. You probably know us.

He slams the door.

GEORGE: I can't say I do.

He points the way and leads off down the drive.

CRONSHAW: Branches everywhere. Far too many, judging by this little how-do-you-do. Anyway, your brother came to our place, wanted something around two-fifty.

GEORGE (*faltering*): Two hundred and fifty pounds?

CRONSHAW (*with a nod*): I had a Meteor 8, '36 model.

33

£275. Lovely job. He took it out for a trial run. We haven't seen him since.

GEORGE: You know my brother?

CRONSHAW: Yes, of course. Wouldn't have taken a chance otherwise. . . . You mean, knowing him, I shouldn't have been such a mug.

GEORGE (*becoming confused*): No, certainly not . . . I wasn't implying . . . (*Stops in his walk and turns to Cronshaw.*) Well, I know my brother's always been on the wild side, but he's never done anything dishonest.

CRONSHAW (*acidly*): I don't know what else you'd call this.

George cannot answer this one. He looks at Cronshaw and then leads the way to the terrace.

73. *Exterior Chartfield Manor. Day.* (*Location.*) *Medium long two shot. Tea table in foreground. They step from driveway onto terrace, walk to table and sit down.*

GEORGE: Did you circulate a description of the car? He might have had an accident.

CRONSHAW: Oh, we've got the car back.

GEORGE (*bewildered*): Then what . . .

CRONSHAW (*both are now in tight two shot*): He sold it to our Berkeley Square branch.

GEORGE (*crushed, sits down*): I'm sorry, do sit down.

Cronshaw sits and the two face each other fifty-fifty.

GEORGE: They made no enquiries? What about the registration papers?

CRONSHAW: I said they paid cash. Buying and selling cars is a tricky business these days. If you're offered a bargain . . .

GEORGE (*unpleasantly*): Tricky seems the right word.

74. *Exterior Chartfield Manor. Day.* (*Location.*) *Over shoulder of George on to Cronshaw.*

CRONSHAW (*getting nasty*): Look here, Mr. Ramsay, how we run our business is entirely beside the point. Your brother has swindled us out of £200 and he's not going to get away with it. The fellow's a scoundrel and I intend to see that he's punished.

He stands up as if to go.

GEORGE: Wait . . .

34

Cronshaw hesitates and then sits down again. On this action, cut round on to George.

75. *Exterior Chartfield Manor. Day. (Location.) Over shoulder of Cronshaw on to George.*

GEORGE: Would you still take that highly moral attitude if you got your money back?

CRONSHAW (*sharply*): Then you do know where he is?

GEORGE (*shaking his head*): I am suggesting that you might be prepared to forget this unfortunate affair if I make good your loss.

76. *Exterior Chartfield Manor. Day. (Location.) Cronshaw brightens up.*

CRONSHAW (*with a note of admiration*): You'd do that? . . . (*Protestingly*) Oh, but no, why should you?

77. *Exterior Chartfield Manor. Day. (Location.) Individual shot of George. With a suppressed sigh he takes a chequebook out of his pocket.*

GEORGE: Much as I disapprove of my brother, I don't wish him to be the first member of our family to go to prison.

CRONSHAW (*his sense of ethics disturbed*): It's not right, you know. The man's a menace . . . he ought to be locked up.

GEORGE (*producing a fountain pen*): How do you sign yourself?

CRONSHAW (*making a half-guilty gesture of acquiescence*): Philip Cronshaw. C-R-O-N——

78. *Insert: Cheque being made out and name Philip Cronshaw written.*

DISSOLVE

79. *Insert: Bundle of notes being pushed under bank-counter grille.*

80. *Exterior Bank London. Day. Cronshaw is counting a bundle of notes with great satisfaction. He looks up at Tom and hands over half the bank notes to him. They scan the street for a taxi. Tom then puts his fingers into his mouth and lets fly with one of his special whistles.*

35

81. *Exterior Long shot of Monte Carlo.*

82. *Exterior terrace of Casino. Monte Carlo. Day. Insert various numerals on piece of paper. Above the numbers we read. Red. Red. Black. Red. Red. Red. Etc. We hold this insert a few feet and then hear Tom's voice, saying:*

TOM: Well, how much have we got left?

CRONSHAW: Forty-seven thousand francs, about forty-five quid. And if you'd done what I suggested and played with the table instead of against it we'd have been well in by now.

83. *Exterior terrace of Casino. Monte Carlo. Day. Two shot Cronshaw and Tom at table on terrace poring over records of the roulette table. Two empty glasses in front of them.*

TOM: Well, no one could have foreseen the last fourteen spins nothing over nineteen and zero coming up twice. You can't compete against a thing like that.

CRONSHAW: Your system certainly can't.

TOM: Well, I never said it was infallible.

CRONSHAW: It's the only thing you didn't say about it. Well, what do we do now?

Tom looks up encouragingly at Cronshaw, but his attention has wandered. He is looking with great interest out camera left. Tom looks in the same direction, reacts and then becomes alert and eager.

TOM: Isn't that Gertrude Wilmot over there?

CRONSHAW: That's right. (*Sadly*) Third richest girl in the world and not a thing anyone can do about it.

TOM (*intrigued*): Don't tell me you know her.

CRONSHAW: I certainly do.

TOM: Well, for heaven's sake, man, introduce me.

CRONSHAW: Waste of time, old boy.

TOM: That's the one thing we've got plenty of. Now come on, do your stuff, you've got about ten seconds.

CRONSHAW: You can count yourself *out*. Gertrude's a tough character. She can spot our sort a mile off.

TOM: Come on, come.

CRONSHAW: You won't get anywhere, I've tried.

TOM: Let me try.
They both stand out of shot. On action cut.

84. *Exterior terrace of Casino. Monte Carlo. Day. Long two shot. Tom and Cronshaw standing and smiling.*
CRONSHAW: Hullo, Gertrude, how are you?
GERTRUDE: Why, hi there, Philip. How's your luck running this year? Broken the bank yet?
CRONSHAW: Hardly that, perhaps, but no complaints so far. Won't you join us? We'd be delighted if you would.
By now camera is only a few feet away and Cronshaw introduces Tom.
CRONSHAW: May I introduce a very old friend of mine, Tom Ramsay.
Cronshaw takes a side step, allowing Tom to become centre screen. He gives a slight bow and holds out his hand.
TOM: How do you do, Miss Wilmot.

85. *Exterior terrace of Casino. Monte Carlo. Day. Gertrude is smiling at Tom with a slightly cynical expression.*
GERTRUDE: How do you do, Mr. Ramsay.

86. *Exterior terrace of Casino. Monte Carlo. Day. Tom helps Gertrude to her chair; a waiter passes and Tom stops him.*
TOM: How about champagne cocktails? Suit everyone? You get them, Philip.
Cronshaw exits.

87. *Exterior terrace of Casino. Monte Carlo. Day. Two shot Gertrude and Tom.*
TOM: *This* is wonderful.
GERTRUDE: What is?
TOM: Meeting you at last.
GERTRUDE: Don't tell me, I think I know. You picked up an old newspaper on some distant battlefield and there was a picture of me in it. From that moment you knew what love was.
TOM (*nodding*): Almost—not quite. The first time I read about you, they didn't run a picture. What I fell for was something they said about you.

37

GERTRUDE: Never trust a newspaper report. What was it?

88. *Exterior terrace of Casino. Monte Carlo. Day.*
TOM: They mentioned your bank balance.

89. *Exterior terrace of Casino. Monte Carlo. Day. For a moment she is stunned by the frankness of this admission. Then she roars with laughter.*

TOM (*allowing no interruptions*): Please don't make fun of me. You can't imagine the torture I went through. To fall in love with a bank balance, knowing nothing of the woman behind it . . .

There is no doubt that she is vastly amused by this extraordinary outpouring.

TOM: Whether she was short and fat with legs like a piano, or if perhaps she had a cavalry moustache.

TOM (*brightening*): And then—and then the glorious day when I *did* see your photograph and you were beautiful.

GERTRUDE: Go on. This is terrific.

TOM (*his enthusiasm mounting*): And now—today. I meet you at last and I find you're intelligent too. All the virtues I've looked for in the woman I mean to make my wife.

GERTRUDE: Hey, just a minute . . .

TOM (*leans forward and takes her hand*): Miss Wilmot —or may I say Gertrude? Don't keep me in suspense any longer. Name the day, lend me the money for the licence . . .

(*Off screen*) Here are your drinks.

TOM (*looking over shoulder*): Quiet, please, there's a man proposing. (*Turns back to Gertrude.*) Where was I?

GERTRUDE: Never mind. There's something I'd like to know . . .

TOM (*releasing her hand and waving a courteous gesture*): Please.

GERTRUDE: This woman without a flaw—what does she get out of it all?

TOM (*leaning back as waiter places drinks on table*): A man without any redeeming qualities whatever, which is something exceedingly rare.

38

90. *Exterior terrace of Casino. Monte Carlo. Day. Individual of Gertrude.*

GERTRUDE (*smiling at him she raises her glass*): Never mind, Mr. Ramsay—you certainly have a new approach.

91. *Exterior terrace of Casino. Monte Carlo. Day. Individual of Tom.*

TOM: Meaning that none of my rivals ever sink so low as to mention your money?

GERTRUDE: It's quite the *last* thing they're interested in.

TOM (*shaking his head*): Very poor technique.

GERTRUDE (*looking at him appraisingly*): Do you really think you're doing better?

TOM: I've seen longer shots come up.

FADE OUT

92. *Exterior Chartfield Manor. Day. George is having breakfast on the terrace.* The Times *is propped up in front of him. There is evidence that the house is in process of being stripped for the impending removal. We open on a medium shot of George at breakfast as Freda walks from the drive round the corner of the house up to the table, with a pile of receipts.*

FREDA: George, I'm clearing out the desk in the ante-room. Do we have to keep all these old receipts?

GEORGE (*without looking up*): It depends how far back they go. Any that we've had for more than six years . . .

FREDA (*now at table and looking down at George querulously*): But that will mean going through them all . . .

George suddenly explodes into his coffee over something he sees in The Times.

GEORGE: *Good heavens!*

FREDA: What?

GEORGE: Well, I'll be . . .

Freda hurries to look at the paper and is startled out of her wits as George crashes his fist on the table.

GEORGE: I don't understand it. (*He snatches up the paper.*) How can these things *be?*

FREDA: If you don't tell me, George . . .

George thumps the arm of his chair in torment, then gets up and strides away. Turning round to face her, he addresses her in a bitter voice.

39

GEORGE: Freda, you can't deny that all my life I've been hard-working, decent, respectable and straightforward?

FREDA (*nervously*): I know you have, dear.

GEORGE (*still pacing*): And you can't deny that my brother Tom has been an idle, worthless, dissolute and dishonourable rogue. If there were any justice he'd be in the workhouse.

FREDA: Yes, dear, but what . . .

GEORGE (*thrusting paper at her*): Read this. (*He stabs his finger at the spot.*)

FREDA (*reading*): Good gracious! Tom married!

GEORGE: Read it!

FREDA: "to Gertrude, only daughter of the late Mr. Harvey J. Wilmot, of New York . . ." (*Looking up incredulously*) Not *the* Gertrude Wilmot?

93. *Exterior Chartfield Manor. Day. Individual of George. He turns and faces Freda.*

GEORGE: Only the second richest girl in the world.

94. *Exterior Chartfield Manor. Day.*

FREDA: Third, dear.

GEORGE (*still pacing*): Second, third—what does it matter? She's got millions—and what's more, she's damned attractive! It's not fair!

FREDA (*hurt*): George.

GEORGE: It's not fair, I tell you, it's not fair.

(*If there is no window into wall of house facing terrace, we shall have to introduce phone call by arrival of maid, and George will hurry round to front of house and take phone from window, facing driveway. If there is a window where we want it, camera will pan him over to it.*

MAID (*arriving in b.g. of shot*): Excuse me, sir, you're wanted on the phone. It's the office, sir.

95. *Exterior Chartfield Manor. Day.*

GEORGE: What the blazes do they want?

MAID: They didn't say, sir.

George hurriedly walks past camera.

96. *Exterior Chartfield Manor. Day. Medium shot to close shot. George walking round side of house from terrace up to living-room window. He reaches inside and grabs the phone.*

40

GEORGE: Hullo.

He listens for a moment, then his manner changes to sudden eagerness.

GEORGE: He's there now? Keep him there, Miss Farrow. Don't let him go. . . . Yes, at once.

He slams down the receiver.

97. *Exterior Chartfield Manor. Day. Freda is now seated at the table reading* The Times, *and George enters shot as did Freda.*

GEORGE: I'm going to London.

FREDA: But, George, the moving men.

GEORGE: Never mind the moving men. I'm going to get something back out of this.

DISSOLVE

98. *Interior Reception Office. Day. Tom at Miss Farrow's desk with feet up. He is looking exceedingly pleased with himself as he exhales a cloud of smoke. Camera dollies back as we hear footsteps mounting the stairs outside the office. We are in medium shot of desk and door as George bursts through it, immediately noticing Tom.*

GEORGE: Ah!

TOM (*rising at his leisure*): Ah . . . Hullo, George.

GEORGE (*stiffly*): I suppose I ought to congratulate you.

TOM (*grinning*): Well, it really has been quite an achievement.

GEORGE (*gesturing to office*): Come into my office.

As they walk forward—cut to interior of office.

99. *Interior George's Office. Day. Men enter centre background.*

GEORGE: All right, Miss Farrow.

She walks to the door. Tom smiles at her as she approaches and takes her hand as she is about to pass. On action cut in.

100. *Interior George's Office. Day.*

TOM: Cheer up, Patricia, there are just as good fish in the sea.

She snatches her hand away and exits with an angry snort.

41

GEORGE (*annoyed*): I wish, Tom, you'd kindly refrain from . . .

TOM: No more sermons. I've come here for one purpose only. Can you give me some idea of what I owe you?

GEORGE (*taking out little notebook from waistcoat pocket*): I can tell you exactly.

Tom flops into armchair with extreme informality. George has exited from shot as he sits in his chair, but enters again almost at once so that we are shooting over his shoulder on to Tom for his next line.

TOM: Including, of course, what that frightful chap Cronshaw took off you.

GEORGE: Naturally.

TOM: Though I must say, George, you were a bit gullible there.

101. *Interior George's Office. Day. Individual of George. He finishes a mental totting up and looks over at Tom.*

GEORGE: The amount is exactly one thousand two hundred and eighteen pounds, four shillings and sevenpence.

102. *Interior George's Office. Day. Individual of Tom.*

TOM (*producing a new chequebook from breast pocket with the suspicion of a flourish*): Does that include interest?

GEORGE: It does not.

TOM: Right, call it thirteen hundred—I'm easy.

GEORGE: I don't want any favours.

TOM: And I don't want writer's cramp . . . one thousand . . . three hundred . . .

GEORGE: Well, I'm bound to say I never expected to see that money again.

TOM: A gentleman always pays his debts.

GEORGE: Does a gentleman give a false address in his efforts to impress a lady?

TOM (*absently, signing cheque*): I should hope not.

GEORGE: Then will you please explain?

TOM (*tearing out cheque and laying it on desk*): That address, nothing false about it. (*Rises.*) You see, I happened to tell Gertrude about Chartfield, and she rather liked the sound of it—she's always wanted a country house in England. Your friend Bateman didn't need much persuading when he heard our price. He's made a very nice profit on the deal. (*Moves off a couple of steps and then turns back.*) And you, George—you will have the satisfaction of knowing the old place still remains in the family.

George sits at desk speechless with fury.

103. *Interior George's Office. Day. Medium close shot of Tom walking to office door. He turns and waves to George. His hand flops down onto his trouser pocket. He feels his other pocket, reaches the door, opens it, is about to go out, then turns back, looks at George and says*

Tom: I say, George, I seem to have left myself a bit short, could you lend me a fiver?

FADE OUT

THE END

WINTER CRUISE

CAPTAIN Erdmann knew Miss Reid very little till the *Friedrich Weber* reached Haiti. She came on board at Plymouth, but by then he had taken on a number of passengers, French, Belgian and Haitian, many of whom had travelled with him before, and she was placed at the chief engineer's table. The *Friedrich Weber* was a freighter sailing regularly from Hamburg to Cartagena on the Colombian coast and on the way touching at a number of islands in the West Indies. She carried phosphates and cement from Germany and took back coffee and timber; but her owners, the Brothers Weber, were always willing to send her out of her route if a cargo of any sort made it worth their while. The *Friedrich Weber* was prepared to take cattle, mules, potatoes or anything else that offered the chance of earning an honest penny. She carried passengers. There were six cabins on the upper deck and six below. The accommodation was not luxurious, but the food was good, plain and abundant, and the fares were cheap. The round trip took nine weeks and was not costing Miss Reid more than forty-five pounds. She looked forward not only to seeing many interesting places, with historical associations, but also to acquiring a great deal of information that would enrich her mind.

The agent had warned her that till the ship reached Port au Prince in Haiti she would have to share a cabin with another woman. Miss Reid did not mind that, she liked company, and when the steward told her that her companion was a Madame Bollin she thought at once that it would be a very good opportunity to rub up her French. She was only very slightly disconcerted when she found that Madame Bollin was coal black. She told herself that one had to accept the rough with the smooth and that it takes all sorts to make a world. Miss Reid was a good sailor, as indeed was only to be expected since her grandfather had been a naval officer, but after a couple of roughish days the weather was fine and in a very short while she knew all her fellow passengers. She was a good mixer. That was one of the reasons why she had made a success of her business; she owned a tearoom at a celebrated beauty spot in the west of England and she always had a smile and a pleasant word for every customer who came in; she closed down in the winter and for the last four years had taken a cruise. You met such interesting people, she said, and you always learnt something. It was true that the passengers on the *Friedrich Weber* weren't of quite so good a class as those she had met the year before on her Mediterranean cruise, but Miss Reid was not a snob, and though the table manners of some of them shocked her somewhat, determined to look upon the bright side of things, she decided to make the best of them. She was a great reader and she was glad, on looking at the ship's library, to find that there were a lot of books by Phillips Oppenheim, Edgar Wallace and Agatha Christie; but with so many people to talk to she had no time for reading and she made up her mind to leave them till the ship emptied herself at Haiti.

"After all," she said, "human nature is more important than literature."

Miss Reid had always had the reputation of being a good talker and she flattered herself that not once during the many days they were at sea had she allowed the conversation at table to languish. She knew how to draw people out and whenever a topic seemed to be exhausted she had a remark ready to revive it or another topic waiting on the tip of her tongue to set the conversation off again. Her friend Miss Price, daughter of the late Vicar of Campden, who had come to see her off at Plymouth, for she lived there, had often said to her:

"You know, Venetia, you have a mind like a man. You're never at a loss for something to say."

"Well, I think if you're interested in everyone, everyone will be interested in you," Miss Reid answered modestly. "Practice makes perfect and I have the infinite capacity for taking pains which Dickens said was genius."

Miss Reid was not really called Venetia, her name was Alice, but, disliking it, she had, when still a girl, adopted the poetic name which she felt so much better suited to her personality.

Miss Reid had a great many interesting talks with her fellow passengers and she was really sorry when the ship at length reached Port au Prince and the last of them disembarked. The *Friedrich Weber* stopped two days there, during which she visited the town and the neighbourhood. When they sailed she was the only passenger. The ship was skirting the coast of the island, stopping off at a variety of ports to discharge or to take on cargo.

"I hope you will not feel embarrassed alone with so many men, Miss Reid," said the captain heartily as they sat down to midday dinner.

She was placed on his right hand, and at table besides sat the first mate, the chief engineer and the doctor.

"I'm a woman of the world, Captain. I always think if a lady is a lady gentlemen will be gentlemen."

"We're only rough sailormen, madam, you mustn't expect too much."

"Kind hearts are more than coronets and simple faith than Norman blood, Captain," answered Miss Reid.

He was a short, thick-set man, with a clean-shaven head and a red, clean-shaven face. He wore a white stingah-shifter, but except at mealtimes unbuttoned at the neck and showing his hairy chest. He was a jovial fellow. He could not speak without bellowing. Miss Reid thought him quite an eccentric, but she had a keen sense of humour and was prepared to make allowances for that. She took the conversation in hand. She had learnt a great deal about Haiti on the voyage out and more during the two days she had spent there, but she knew that men liked to talk rather than to listen, so she put them a number of questions of which she already knew the answers; oddly enough, they didn't. In the end she found herself obliged to give quite a little lecture and before lunch was over, *Mittag Essen*, they called it in their funny way, she had imparted to them a great deal of interesting information about the history and economic situation of the republic, the problems that confronted it and its prospects for the future. She talked rather slowly, in a refined voice, and her vocabulary was extensive.

At nightfall they put in at a small port where they were to load three hundred bags of coffee and the agent came on board. The captain asked him to stay to supper and ordered cocktails. As the steward brought them Miss Reid swam into the saloon. Her movements were deliberate, elegant and self-assured. She always said that you could tell at once by the way she walked if a woman was a lady. The captain introduced the agent to her and she sat down.

"What is that you men are drinking?" she asked.

"A cocktail. Will you have one, Miss Reid?"

"I don't mind if I do."

She drank it and the captain somewhat doubtfully asked her if she would have another.

"Another? Well, just to be matey."

The agent, much whiter than some, but a good deal darker than many, was the son of a former minister of Haiti to the German court and, having lived for many years in Berlin, spoke good German. It was indeed on this account that he had got a job with a German shipping firm. On the strength of this Miss Reid, during supper, told them all about a trip down the Rhine that she had once taken. Afterwards she and the agent, the skipper, the doctor and the mate sat round a table and drank beer. Miss Reid made it her business to draw the agent out. The fact that they were loading coffee suggested to her that he would be interested in learning how they grew tea in Ceylon—yes, she had been to Ceylon on a cruise—and the fact that his father was a diplomat made it certain that he would be interested in the royal family of England. She had a very pleasant evening. When she at last retired to rest, for she would never have thought of saying she was going to bed, she said to herself:

"There's no doubt that travel is a great education."

It was really an experience to find herself alone with all those men. How they would laugh when she told them all about it when she got home! They would say

48

that things like that only happened to Venetia. She smiled when she heard the captain on deck singing with that great booming voice of his. Germans were so musical. He had a funny way of strutting up and down on his short legs singing Wagner tunes to words of his own invention. It was *Tannhäuser* he was singing now (that lovely thing about the evening star), but knowing no German, Miss Reid could only wonder what absurd words he was putting to it. It was as well.

"Oh, what a bore that woman is. I shall certainly kill her if she goes on much longer." Then he broke into Siegfried's martial strain. "She's a bore, she's a bore, she's a bore. I shall throw her into the sea."

And that of course is what Miss Reid was. She was a crashing, she was a stupendous, she was an excruciating bore. She talked in a steady monotone and it was no use to interrupt her because then she started again from the beginning. She had an insatiable thirst for information and no casual remark could be thrown across the table without her asking innumerable questions about it. She was a great dreamer and she narrated her dreams at intolerable length. There was no subject upon which she had not something prosy to say. She had a truism for every occasion. She hit on the commonplace like a hammer driving a nail into the wall. She plunged into the obvious like a clown in a circus jumping through a hoop. Silence did not abash her. Those poor men far away from their homes and the patter of little feet, and with Christmas coming on, no wonder they felt low; she redoubled her efforts to interest and amuse them. She was determined to bring a little gaiety into their dull lives. For that was the awful part of it. Miss Reid meant well. She was not only having a good time herself, but she was trying to give all of them a good time. She was convinced that they liked her as much as she liked them. She felt that she was doing her bit to make the party a success and she was naïvely happy to think that she was succeeding. She told them all about her friend Miss Price and how often she had said to her, Venetia, no one ever has a dull moment in your company. It was the captain's duty to be polite to a passenger and however much he would have liked to tell her to hold her silly tongue he could not, but even if he had been free to say what he liked, he knew that he could not have brought himself to hurt her feelings. Nothing stemmed the torrent of her loquacity. It was as irresistible as a force of nature. Once, in desperation, they began talking German, but Miss Reid stopped this at once.

"Now I won't have you saying things I don't understand. You ought all to make the most of your good luck in having me all to yourselves and practice your English."

"We were talking of technical matters that would only bore you, Miss Reid," said the captain.

"I'm never bored. That's why, if you won't think me a wee bit conceited to say so, I'm never boring. You see, I like to know things. Everything interests me and you never know when a bit of information won't come in useful."

The doctor smiled drily.

"The captain was only saying that because he was embarrassed. In point of fact, he was telling a story that was not fit for the ears of a maiden lady."

"I may be a maiden lady but I'm also a woman of the world, I don't expect sailors to be saints. You need never be afraid of what you say before me, Captain, I shan't be shocked. I should love to hear your story."

The doctor was a man of sixty with thin grey hair, a

grey moustache and small bright blue eyes. He was a silent, bitter man, and however hard Miss Reid tried to bring him into the conversation it was almost impossible to get a word out of him. But she wasn't a woman who would give in without a struggle and one morning when they were at sea, seeing him sitting on deck with a book, she brought her chair next to his and sat down beside him.

"Are you fond of reading, Doctor?" she said brightly.

"Yes."

"So am I. And I suppose like all Germans you're musical."

"I'm fond of music."

"So am I. The moment I saw you I thought you looked clever."

He gave her a brief look and, pursing his lips, went on reading. Miss Reid was not disconcerted.

"But of course one can always read. I always prefer a good talk to a good book. Don't you?"

"No."

"How very interesting. Now do tell me why."

"I can't give you a reason."

"That's very strange, isn't it? But then I always think human nature is strange. I'm terribly interested in people, you know. I always like doctors, they know so much about human nature, but I could tell you some things that would surprise even you. You learn a great deal about people if you run a teashop like I do, that's to say if you keep your eyes open."

The doctor got up.

"I must ask you to excuse me, Miss Reid. I have to go and see a patient."

"Anyhow, I've broken the ice now," she thought as he walked away. "I think he was only shy."

51

But a day or two later the doctor was not feeling at all well. He had an internal malady that troubled him now and then, but he was used to it and disinclined to talk about it. When he had one of his attacks he only wanted to be left alone. His cabin was small and stuffy, so he settled himself on a long chair on deck and lay with his eyes closed. Miss Reid was walking up and down to get the half hour's exercise she took morning and evening. He thought that if he pretended to be asleep she would not disturb him. But when she had passed him half a dozen times she stopped in front of him and stood quite still. Though he kept his eyes closed he knew that she was looking at him.

"Is there anything I can do, Doctor?" she said.

He started.

"Why, what should there be?"

He gave her a glance and saw that her eyes were deeply troubled.

"You look dreadfully ill," she said.

"I'm in great pain."

"I know. I can see that. Can't something be done?"

"No, it'll pass off presently."

She hesitated for a moment, then went away. Presently she returned.

"You look so uncomfortable with no cushions or anything. I've brought you my own pillow that I always travel with. Do let me put it behind your head."

He felt at that moment too ill to remonstrate. She lifted his head gently and put the soft pillow behind it. It really did make him feel more comfortable. She passed her hand across his forehead and it was cool and soft.

"Poor dear," she said. "I know what doctors are. They haven't the first idea how to take care of themselves."

52

She left him, but in a minute or two returned with a chair and a bag. The doctor when he saw her gave a twitch of anguish.

"Now I'm not going to let you talk, I'm just going to sit beside you and knit. I always think it's a comfort when one isn't feeling very well to have someone near."

She sat down and, taking an unfinished muffler out of her bag, began busily to ply her needles. She never said a word. And strangely enough the doctor found her company a solace. No one else on board had even noticed that he was ill, he had felt lonely, and the sympathy of that crashing bore was grateful to him. It soothed him to see her silently working and presently he fell asleep. When he awoke she was still working. She gave him a little smile, but did not speak. His pain had left him and he felt much better.

He did not go into the saloon till late in the afternoon. He found the captain and Hans Krause, the mate, having a glass of beer together.

"Sit down, Doctor," said the captain. "We're holding a council of war. You know that the day after tomorrow is *Sylvester Abend*.

"Of course."

Sylvester Abend, New Year's Eve, is an occasion that means a great deal to a German and they had all been looking forward to it. They had brought a Christmas tree all the way from Germany with them.

"At dinner today Miss Reid was more talkative than ever. Hans and I have decided that something must be done about it."

"She sat with me for two hours this morning in silence. I suppose she was making up for lost time."

"It's bad enough to be away from one's home and family just now anyway, and all we can do is to make

53

the best of a bad job. We want to enjoy our *Sylvester Abend* and unless something is done about Miss Reid we haven't a chance."

"We can't have a good time if she's with us," said the mate. "She'll spoil it as sure as eggs is eggs."

"How do you propose to get rid of her short of throwing her overboard?" smiled the doctor. "She's not a bad old soul; all she wants is a lover."

"At her age?" cried Hans Krause.

"Especially at her age. That inordinate loquacity, that passion for information, the innumerable questions she asks, her prosiness, the way she goes on and on—it is all a sign of her clamouring virginity. A lover would bring her peace. Those jangled nerves of hers would relax. At least for an hour she would have lived. The deep satisfaction which her being demands would travel through those exacerbated centres of speech and we should have quiet."

It was always a little difficult to know how much the doctor meant what he said and when he was having a joke at your expense. The captain's blue eyes, however, twinkled mischievously.

"Well, Doctor, I have great confidence in your powers of diagnosis. The remedy you suggest is evidently worth trying and since you are a bachelor it is clear that it is up to you to apply it."

"Pardon me, Captain, it is my professional duty to prescribe remedies for the patients under my charge in this ship but not to administer them personally. Besides, I am sixty."

"I am a married man with grown-up children," said the captain. "I am old and fat and asthmatic; it is obvious that I cannot be expected to undertake a task of this kind. Nature cut me out for the role of a husband or a father, not for that of a lover."

"Youth in these matters is essential and good looks are advantageous," said the doctor gravely.

The captain gave a great bang on the table with his fist.

"You are thinking of Hans. You're quite right. Hans must do it."

The mate sprang to his feet.

"Me? Never."

"Hans, you are tall, handsome, strong as a lion, brave and young. We have twenty-three days more at sea before we reach Hamburg; you wouldn't desert your trusted old captain in an emergency or let down your good friend the doctor?"

"No, Captain, it's asking too much of me. I have been married less than a year and I love my wife. I can hardly wait to get back to Hamburg. She is yearning for me as I am yearning for her. I will not be unfaithful to her, especially with Miss Reid."

"Miss Reid's not so bad," said the doctor.

"Some people might call her even nice-looking," said the captain.

And indeed when you took Miss Reid feature by feature she was not in fact a plain woman. True that she had a long, stupid face, but her brown eyes were large and she had very thick lashes; her brown hair was cut short and curled rather prettily over her neck; she hadn't a bad skin, and she was neither too fat nor too thin. She was not old as people go nowadays and if she had told you that she was forty you would have been quite willing to believe it. The only thing against her was that she was drab and dull.

"Must I then for twenty-three mortal days endure the prolixity of that tedious woman? Must I for twenty-three mortal days answer her inane questions and listen to her fatuous remarks? Must I, an old man, have my *Sylvester Abend*, the jolly evening I was looking forward to, ruined by the unwelcome company of that intolerable virgin? And all because no one can be found to show a little gallantry, a little human kindness, a spark of charity to a lonely woman. I shall wreck the ship."

"There's always the radio operator," said Hans.

The captain gave a great shout.

"Hans, let the ten thousand virgins of Cologne arise and call you blessed. Steward," he bellowed, "tell the radio operator that I want him."

The radio operator came into the saloon and smartly clicked his heels together. The three men looked at him in silence. He wondered uneasily whether he had done something for which he was to be hauled over the coals. He was above the middle height, with square shoulders and narrow hips, erect and slender; his tanned, smooth skin looked as though a razor had never touched it; he had large eyes of a startling blue and a mane of curling golden hair. He was a perfect specimen of young Teutonic manhood. He was so healthy, so vigorous, so much alive that even when he stood some way from you, you felt the glow of his vitality.

"Aryan, all right," said the captain. "No doubt about that. How old are you, my boy?"

"Twenty-one, sir."

"Married?"

"No, sir."

"Engaged?"

The radio operator chuckled. There was an engaging boyishness in his laugh.

"No, sir."

"You know that we have a female passenger on board?"

"Yes, sir."

"Do you know her?"

"I've said good morning to her when I've seen her on deck."

The captain assumed his most official manner. His eyes, which generally twinkled with fun, were stern and he got a sort of bark into his rich, fruity voice.

"Although this is a cargo boat and we carry valuable freight, we also take such passengers as we can get, and this is a branch of our business that the company is anxious to encourage. My instructions are to do everything possible to promote the happiness and comfort of the passengers. Miss Reid needs a lover. The doctor and I have come to the conclusion that you are well suited to satisfy Miss Reid's requirements."

"Me, sir?"

The radio operator blushed scarlet and then began to giggle, but quickly composed himself when he saw the set faces of the three men who confronted him.

"But she's old enough to be my mother."

"That, at your age, is a matter of no consequence. She is a woman of the highest distinction and allied to all the great families of England. If she were German she would be at least a countess. That you should have been chosen for this responsible position is an honour that you should greatly appreciate. Furthermore, your English is halting and this will give you an excellent opportunity to improve it."

"That, of course, is something to be thought of," said the radio operator. "I know that I want practice."

"It is not often in this life that it is possible to combine pleasure with intellectual improvement and you must congratulate yourself on your good fortune."

"But if I may be allowed to put the question, sir, why does Miss Reid want a lover?"

"It appears to be an old English custom for unmar-

57

ried women of exalted rank to submit themselves to the embraces of a lover at this time of year. The company is anxious that Miss Reid should be treated exactly as she would be on an English ship and we trust that if she is satisfied, with her aristocratic connections she will be able to persuade many of her friends to take cruises in the line's ships."

"Sir, I must ask to be excused."

"It is not a request that I am making, it is an order. You will present yourself to Miss Reid, in her cabin, at eleven o'clock tonight."

"What shall I do when I get there?"

"Do?" thundered the captain. "Do? Act naturally."

With a wave of the hand he dismissed him. The radio operator clicked his heels, saluted and went out.

"Now let us have another glass of beer," said the captain.

At supper that evening Miss Reid was at her best. She was verbose. She was playful. She was refined. There was not a truism that she failed to utter. There was not a commonplace that she forebore to express. She bombarded them with foolish questions. The captain's face grew redder and redder as he sought to contain his fury; he felt that he could not go on being polite to her any longer and if the doctor's remedy did not help, one day he would forget himself and give her, not a piece, but the whole of his mind.

"I shall lose my job," he thought, "but I'm not sure that it wouldn't be worth it."

Next day they were already sitting at table when she came in to dinner.

"*Sylvester Abend* tomorrow," she said brightly. That was the sort of thing she would say. She went on: "Well, what have you all been up to this morning?"

Since they did exactly the same thing every day,

and she knew very well what that was, the question was infuriating. The captain's heart sank. He briefly told the doctor what he thought of him.

"Now, no German, please," said Miss Reid archly. "You know I don't allow that, and why, Captain, did you give the poor doctor that sour look? It's Christmas time, you know; peace and good will to all men. I'm so excited about tomorrow evening and will there be candles on the Christmas tree?"

"Naturally."

"How thrilling! I always think a Christmas tree without candles isn't a Christmas tree. Oh, d'you know, I had such a funny experience last night. I can't understand it at all."

A startled pause. They all looked intently at Miss Reid. For once they hung on her lips.

"Yes," she went on in that monotonous, rather finicking way of hers, "I was just getting into bed last night when there was a knock at my door. 'Who is it?' I said. 'It's the radio operator,' was the answer. 'What is it?' I said. 'Can I speak to you?' he said."

They listened with rapt attention.

" 'Well, I'll just pop on a dressing gown,' I said, 'and open the door.' So I popped on a dressing gown and opened the door. The radio operator said, 'Excuse me, miss, but do you want to send a radio?' Well, I did think it was funny his coming at that hour to ask me if I wanted to send a radio, I just laughed in his face, it appealed to my sense of humour if you understand what I mean, but I didn't want to hurt his feelings so I said, 'Thank you so much, but I don't think I want to send a radio.' He stood there, looking so funny, as if he was quite embarrassed, so I said, 'Thank you all the same for asking me,' and then I said, 'Good night, pleasant dreams,' and shut the door."

"The damned fool," cried the captain.

"He's young, Miss Reid," the doctor put in. "It was excess of zeal. I suppose he thought you would want to send a New Year's greeting to your friends and he wished you to get the advantage of the special rate."

"Oh, I didn't mind at all. I like these queer little things that happen to one when one's travelling. I just get a good laugh out of them."

As soon as dinner was over and Miss Reid had left them the captain sent for the radio operator.

"You idiot, what in heaven's name made you ask Miss Reid last night whether she wanted to send a radio?"

"Sir, you told me to act naturally. I am a radio operator. I thought it natural to ask her if she wanted to send a radio. I didn't know what else to say."

"God in heaven," shouted the captain, "when Siegfried saw Brünnhilde lying on her rock and cried: *Das ist kein mann*," the captain sang the words and, being pleased with the sound of his voice, repeated the phrase two or three times before he continued, "did Siegfried when she awoke ask her if she wished to send a radio, to announce to her papa, I suppose, that she was sitting up after her long sleep and taking notice?"

"I beg most respectfully to draw your attention to the fact that Brünnhilde was Siegfried's aunt. Miss Reid is a total stranger to me."

"He did not reflect that she was his aunt. He knew only that she was a beautiful and defenceless woman of obviously good family and he acted as any gentleman would have done. You are young, handsome, Aryan to the tips of your fingers, the honour of Germany is in your hands."

"Very good, sir. I will do my best."

That night there was another knock on Miss Reid's door.

"Who is it?"

"The radio operator. I have a radio for you, Miss Reid."

"For me." She was surprised, but it at once occurred to her that one of her fellow passengers who had got off at Haiti had sent her New Year's greetings. "How very kind people are," she thought. "I'm in bed. Leave it outside the door."

"It needs an answer. Ten words prepaid."

Then it couldn't be a New Year's greeting. Her heart stopped beating. It could only mean one thing: her shop had been burned to the ground. She jumped out of bed.

"Slip it under the door and I'll write the answer and slip it back to you."

The envelope was pushed under the door and as it appeared on the carpet it had really a sinister look. Miss Reid snatched it up and tore the envelope open. The words swam before her eyes and she couldn't for a moment find her spectacles. This is what she read:

"Happy New Year. Stop. Peace and good will to all men. Stop. You are very beautiful. Stop. I love you. Stop. I must speak to you. Stop. Signed: Radio Operator."

Miss Reid read this through twice. Then she slowly took off her spectacles and hid them under a scarf. She opened the door.

"Come in," she said.

Next day was New Year's Eve. The officers were cheerful and a little sentimental when they sat down to dinner (*Mittag Essen* as they called it in their funny way). The stewards had decorated the saloon with

61

tropical creepers to make up for holly and mistletoe, and the Christmas tree stood on a table with the candles ready to be lit at suppertime. Miss Reid did not come in till the officers were seated and when they bade her good morning she did not speak but merely bowed. They looked at her curiously. She ate a good dinner, but uttered never a word. Her silence was uncanny. At last the captain could stand it no longer, and he said:

"You're very quiet today, Miss Reid."

"I'm thinking," she remarked.

"And will you not tell us your thoughts, Miss Reid?" the doctor asked playfully.

She gave him a cool, you might almost have called it a supercilious, look.

"I prefer to keep them to myself, Doctor. I will have a little more of that hash, I've got a very good appetite."

They finished the meal in a blessed silence. The captain heaved a sigh of relief. That was what mealtime was for, to eat, not to chatter. When they had finished he went up to the doctor and wrung his hand.

"Something has happened, Doctor."

"It has happened. She's a changed woman."

"But will it last?"

"One can only hope for the best."

Miss Reid put on an evening dress for the evening's celebration, a very quiet black dress, with artificial roses at her bosom and a long string of imitation jade round her neck. The lights were dimmed and the candles on the Christmas tree were lit. It felt a little like being in church. The junior officers were supping in the saloon that evening and they looked very smart in their white uniforms. Champagne was served at the company's expense and after supper they had a *mai-bowle*. They pulled crackers. They sang songs to the gramophone, "Deutschland," "Deutschland über Alles," "Alt Heidelberg" and "Auld Lang Syne." They shouted out the tunes lustily, the captain's voice rising loud above the others, and Miss Reid joining in with a pleasing contralto. The doctor noticed that Miss Reid's eyes from time to time rested on the radio operator and in them he read an expression of some bewilderment.

"He's a good-looking fellow, isn't he?" said the doctor.

Miss Reid turned round and looked at the doctor coolly.

"Who?"

"The radio operator. I thought you were looking at him."

"Which is he?"

"The duplicity of women," the doctor muttered, but with a smile he answered: "He's sitting next to the chief engineer."

"Oh, of course, I recognize him now. You know, I never think it matters what a man looks like. I'm so much more interested in a man's brain than in his looks."

"Ah," said the doctor.

They all got a little tight, including Miss Reid, but she did not lose her dignity and when she bade them good night it was in her best manner.

"I've had a very delightful evening. I shall never forget my New Year's Eve on a German boat. It's been very interesting. Quite an experience."

She walked steadily to the door and this was something of a triumph, for she had drunk drink for drink with the rest of them through the evening.

They were all somewhat jaded next day. When the captain, the mate, the doctor and the chief engineer came down to dinner they found Miss Reid already seated. Before each place was a small parcel tied up in pink ribbon. On each was written: "Happy New Year." They gave Miss Reid a questioning glance.

"You've all been so very kind to me I thought I'd like to give each of you a little present. There wasn't much choice at Port au Prince, so you mustn't expect too much."

There was a pair of briar pipes for the captain, half a dozen silk handkerchiefs for the doctor, a cigar case for the mate and a couple of ties for the chief engineer. They had dinner and Miss Reid retired to her cabin to rest. The officers looked at one another uncomfortably. The mate fiddled with the cigar case she had given him.

"I'm a little ashamed of myself," he said at last.

The captain was pensive and it was plain that he too was a trifle uneasy.

"I wonder if we ought to have played that trick on Miss Reid," he said. "She's a good old soul and she's not rich; she's a woman who earns her own living. She must have spent the best part of a hundred marks on these presents. I almost wish we'd left her alone."

The doctor shrugged his shoulders.

"You wanted her silenced and I've silenced her."

"When all's said and done, it wouldn't have hurt us to listen to her chatter for three weeks more," said the mate.

"I'm not happy about her," added the captain. "I feel there's something ominous in her quietness."

She had spoken hardly a word during the meal they had just shared with her. She seemed scarcely to listen to what they said.

"Don't you think you ought to ask her if she's feeling quite well, Doctor?" suggested the captain.

"Of course she's feeling quite well. She's eating like a wolf. If you want enquiries made you'd much better make them of the radio operator."

"You may not be aware of it, Doctor, but I am a man of great delicacy."

"I am a man of heart myself," said the doctor.

For the rest of the journey those men spoilt Miss Reid outrageously. They treated her with the consideration they would have shown to someone who was convalescent after a long and dangerous illness. Though her appetite was excellent they sought to tempt her with new dishes. The doctor ordered wine and insisted on her sharing his bottle with him. They played dominoes with her. They played chess with her. They played bridge with her. They engaged her in conversation. But there was no doubt about it, though she responded to their advances with politeness, she kept herself to herself. She seemed to regard them with something very like disdain; you might almost have thought that she looked upon those men and their efforts to be amiable as pleasantly ridiculous. She seldom spoke unless spoken to. She read detective stories and at night sat on deck looking at the stars. She lived a life of her own.

At last the journey drew to its close. They sailed up the English Channel on a still grey day; they sighted land. Miss Reid packed her trunk. At two o'clock in the afternoon they docked at Plymouth. The captain, the mate and the doctor came along to say good-bye to her.

"Well, Miss Reid," said the captain in his jovial way, "we're sorry to lose you, but I suppose you're glad to be getting home."

"You've been very kind to me, you've all been very kind to me, I don't know what I've done to deserve it.

I've been very happy with you. I shall never forget you."

She spoke rather shakily, she tried to smile, but her lips quivered, and tears ran down her cheeks. The captain got very red. He smiled awkwardly.

"May I kiss you, Miss Reid?"

She was taller than he by half a head. She bent down and he planted a fat kiss on one wet cheek and a fat kiss on the other. She turned to the mate and the doctor. They both kissed her.

"What an old fool I am," she said. "Everybody's so good."

She dried her eyes and slowly, in her graceful, rather absurd way, walked down the companion. The captain's eyes were wet. When she reached the quay she looked up and waved to someone on the boat deck.

"Who's she waving to?" asked the captain.

"The radio operator."

Miss Price was waiting on the quay to welcome her. When they had passed the customs and got rid of Miss Reid's heavy luggage they went to Miss Price's house and had an early cup of tea. Miss Reid's train did not start till five. Miss Price had much to tell Miss Reid.

"But it's too bad of me to go on like this when you've just come home. I've been looking forward to hearing all about your journey."

"I'm afraid there's not very much to tell."

"I can't believe that. Your trip was a success, wasn't it?"

"A distinct success. It was very nice."

"And you didn't mind being with all those Germans?"

"Of course they're not like English people. One has to get used to their ways. They sometimes do things that—well, that English people wouldn't do, you know.

But I always think that one has to take things as they come."

"What sort of things do you mean?"

Miss Reid looked at her friend calmly. Her long, stupid face had a placid look and Miss Price never noticed that in the eyes was a strangely mischievous twinkle.

"Things of no importance really. Just funny, unexpected, rather nice things. There's no doubt that travel is a wonderful education."

WINTER CRUISE

List of Cast

Character	Artiste
MISS REID	KAY WALSH
CAPTAIN	NOEL PURCELL
DOCTOR	RONALD SQUIRE
CHIEF ENGINEER	JOHN LAURIE
PIERRE	JACQUES FRANÇOIS
MATE	JOHN HORSLEY
MISS PRICE	JOAN HARBEN
JUNIOR OFFICER	JOHN WARREN
RADIO OFFICER	GEORGE WINDYEATT
MRS. BALLANTYNE	VERA COOK
DAPHNE BALLANTYNE	CAROL WOLVERIDGE
MR. BALLANTYNE	JOHN BOXER
MRS. ROBINSON	MURIEL GEORGE
MR. ROBINSON	WILFRID CAITHNESS
HONEYMOON GIRL	BRENDA HOGAN
HONEYMOON BOY	VINCENT BALL
COLOURED STEWARDESS	MALVENA FRASER

1. MR. MAUGHAM: "Winter Cruise" was suggested to me by a woman I met on a journey in the South Seas. She had a heart of gold, but she was a crashing bore. I avoided her like the plague, but I couldn't help liking her, and I hope you will too.

2. *Insert. Insert of the book—opening paragraph.*

NARRATOR: Miss Reid owned a tearoom at a celebrated beauty spot in the west of England. She closed down in the winter and for the last four years had taken a cruise.

3. *Exterior London River. Day. (Location.) General shots —docks, quay, etc.*

4. *Exterior London River. Day. (Location.) General shots of the ship—lying alongside the West India Dock.*

5. *Exterior English quayside. Day. (Location.) Cargo being loaded. (This is the personal cargo—and the First Officer (Mate) is soon to be in charge of operations.)*

6. *Exterior Interior English quayside (shed). Day. Tracking shot. General bustle. Miss Reid and Miss Price are crossing towards a door leading on to the dockside.*

MISS REID: Well, now those formalities are over, all I have to do is board the lugger.

MISS PRICE: It looks a nice ship.

MISS REID (*cutting in*): Cargo, of course. Just a few passengers. I do think it was kind of you to come and meet my train, Nora.

MISS PRICE (*eagerly*): I do wish I were coming with you.

By now they have reached the foot of the gangway.

MISS REID: I think I'd better say good-bye to you *now*, dear. (*Kissing her.*) Au revoir!

MISS PRICE: Good-bye, Molly, and don't forget I'll want to know all the details. . . .

Miss Reid has already started up the gangway and Miss Price is left calling her last line after her.

MISS PRICE: Things always seem to happen to you that could *only* happen to you.

MISS REID (*waving—from the top of the gangway*): Good-bye!

MISS PRICE: Bon voyage.

Miss Reid has reached the deck of the vessel, where she is greeted by the officer on duty.

7. *Exterior English quayside. Day. (Location.) The ship. General bustle. Preparations for getting under way. Loading of cargo is completed.*

8. *Exterior Bridge. Day. The Captain, a junior officer and a pilot are on the bridge.*

9. *Exterior ship's deck and gangway. Day. Miss Reid is welcomed at the top of the gangway by a junior officer. Led by Pierre, the steward (who takes her hand luggage from her), she walks along the deck and down a companionway. She is looking about her with interest.*

10. *Interior passage and Miss Reid's Cabin. Day. At the bottom of a companionway Miss Reid and Pierre are joined by a coloured stewardess, who takes over from Pierre and shows Miss Reid into her cabin. Miss Reid is a little disconcerted.*

  (NOTE: *Scenes 11, 12 and 13 to establish passengers and senior officers.*)

11. *Exterior English quayside. Day. (Location.) The ship preparing to sail.*

12. *Exterior English quayside. Day. (Location.) The ship passing through the dock gates and up the London river.*

DISSOLVE

13. *Interior Dining Saloon. Day. The Captain, on behalf of the Company, is introducing his officers to the passengers.*
  CAPTAIN: . . . and just so as you know who the rest of us are, I'm the Captain—— (*There is a ripple of amusement from passengers and personnel.*) Yon good-lookin' man's the chief engineer—yon's the mate—and yon dour man is one I hope you'll only meet socially—the ship's doctor. And now it just remains for me to wish you all a happy and comfortable trip.
  Everyone is about to disperse happily, when Miss Reid steps forward.
  MISS REID: May I take it upon myself to thank the Captain on behalf of all of us for his delightful speech of welcome. Speaking as a traveller who, if I may say so, knows the ropes, I always feel that the happiness and harmony of a trip depend just as much on the passengers as on

70

the crew and so, personally, I intend to banish all silly old standoffishness and be really hail-fellow-well-met with each and every one on board.

The chief engineer looks at the doctor, who quietly raises his eyes to heaven. Cover shots as follows:

14. *Medium shot, favouring the Captain and the officers.*

15. *Medium shot—passengers' reaction.*

16. *Group shot, favouring Miss Reid.*

17. *Medium shot—the Captain and officers reacting to Miss Reid's speech.*

DISSOLVE

18. *Interior Dining Saloon. Day. Crane shot—starting in close shot of Miss Reid. The passengers are in the middle of their first meal (the steward, Pierre, is seen serving). Everybody is in good spirits except Mr. Robinson, who sits glumly with a plate of boiled carrots and a glass of milk. Miss Reid's voice is heard above the general conversation.*

MISS REID: . . . so, fifteen years ago, I opened a little teashop at Benchester. It's called "Molly's Parlour" and . . . Do you know where the cathedral is? Well, "Molly's Parlour" is first on the right and then you go on straight ahead and there it is on your left. It really is quite charming, though I say it myself. A bow window and little leaded panes—and though one might say it's tucked away, we *always* seem to be full—but it's never too full for *me*. I suppose that's because I'm so interested in people, and running a teashop, one really does get to know a lot about people. So many different types, you know—dropping in all the time . . .

During this, on the movement of the steward serving the soup, the camera had pulled back from Miss Reid to bring the Captain, the doctor and chief engineer into foreground.

CAPTAIN (*grumbling*): Ever been in the Brazilian jungle, Doctor?

DOCTOR: No. Why?

CAPTAIN: I was thinking of the parrots (*looking down the table towards Miss Reid*). The only difference between them and yon woman is that parrots stop at nightfall.

71

19. *Group shot. The others react to Miss Reid. Mr. Robinson (in foreground) shoots her a look of deep and unqualified loathing.*

20. *Group shot. The captain and the officers.*
CAPTAIN: Happily we'll not see much of her. There's rough weather ahead.

21. *High seas and deserted decks (stock shot).*

22. *The ship in rough weather (stock shot).*

23. *Exterior section of upper deck. Day. (On rockers.) (This is a special section of the deck on rockers, with wind and spray.) By the companionway leading up onto the bridge stand the Captain and the doctor.*
CAPTAIN (*smiling*): Busy?
DOCTOR: Very!
CAPTAIN: Passengers confined to bunks? Splendid!
Miss Reid comes briskly round a corner.
MISS REID: Good morning! Isn't this fun?
The captain and the doctor, disconcerted, turn to her.
CAPTAIN: It doesna worry you?
MISS REID: Oh, this is nothing.
CAPTAIN: It'll likely get worse.
MISS REID: A real gale? What fun! (*The Captain and the doctor look at one another.*) Oh, Captain, I was wondering whether you and the doctor would like to play bridge after dinner?
CAPTAIN: Well . . .
MISS REID (*not waiting for a reply*): I'm not very good, but what I say is, after all it's only a game.
DOCTOR: I'm afraid . . . my patients . . .
CAPTAIN (*speaking with doctor*): I'll be busy after dinner . . .
MISS REID: Well—we'll see.
Continuing with her walk, she moved away from them and out of frame. The camera tracks in to the captain and the doctor.

DISSOLVE

24. *Interior ship's lounge. Night. (Rockers.) The camera starts on the captain and the doctor and tracks back to*

include Miss Reid and the chief engineer, who are playing bridge.

Miss Reid: Oh dear! Now I've made *another* silly mistake.

Captain (*her partner—not too politely*): Yes, you have!

Miss Reid: Now, now! I seemed to notice our Captain making a little mistake when he played his ten.

Captain (*indignant*): That was no mistake. It was to let you know . . .

Miss Reid: Yes! But as I've never heard of that way of letting somebody know something, I couldn't very well *know* it, could I?

The officer's react to Miss Reid's method of playing bridge.

DISSOLVE

25. *Shot of rougher seas (stock shot).*

26. *Ship in rougher seas (stock shot).*

27. *Shot of mountainous seas (stock shot).*

28. *Interior Captain's cabin. Night. (Rockers.) The Captain is sitting working. The weather is still very rough. The door opens, and the doctor enters, shutting the door with difficulty. A buzzer sounds. The captain answers the telephone.*

Captain (*to doctor*): A message from Miss Reid! Would we like to play bridge? (*Into telephone*) Tell her we're seasick. Aye—both of us!

FADE OUT

FADE IN

29. *Sun rising over a calm sea (stock shot).*

30. *Exterior upper deck. Day. Calm, sunlight and sparkling sea. The Ballantynes are sitting in deck chairs, reading. Daphne is playing with a doll. Mrs. Robinson sits a little further along, with the doctor one chair away from her. In the background is a honeymoon couple—they are playing deck tennis (or shuffleboard). Miss Reid comes along the deck and stops for a moment in front of the Ballantynes.*

73

Miss Reid: Well, this is better, isn't it? And so much warmer. One can *feel* Jamaica getting closer. Quite a tropical touch in the air.

Mrs. Ballantyne: Yes.

Miss Reid (*to Daphne*): And how are *we* this morning?

Daphne: I'm all right. My doll's been seasick.

Miss Reid: Oh dear, oh dear!

Daphne: How old are you?

Mrs. Ballantyne: Daphne!

Miss Reid (*pleasantly*): How old do you think I am?

Daphne: Eighty-seven.

Mrs. Ballantyne: Daphne!

Mrs. Ballantyne drags Daphne away to play shuffleboard. Miss Reid, momentarily put out, waves to Mrs. Robinson, who is sitting with the doctor a few chairs away. She crosses to Mrs. Robinson, the camera panning with her, excluding the deck tennis and shuffleboard.

Miss Reid: Hello. (*Approaching them.*) Good morning, Mrs. Robinson.

Miss Reid sits. The doctor unwisely opens one eye.

Miss Reid: Good morning, Doctor! I thought you were sleeping.

Doctor: No. Not now!

Mrs. Robinson: Where are you staying in Jamaica, Miss Reid?

Miss Reid (*taking out her knitting*): Oh, I'm not staying. I'm making the round trip. Can't be too long away from "Molly's Parlour."

Mrs. Robinson: I think it's so clever of you to run a teashop. I'd love to do it, but I haven't got the grasp.

Miss Reid: I must say it does need a certain amount of organizing ability. But, although I say it myself, I think I have got that. (*She laughs modestly.*) My great friend, Miss Price, always says I very nearly have a man's mind.

She turns to the doctor.

Miss Reid: Do you think that's a bad thing, Doctor?

Doctor: Not at all! My great-aunt Louise very nearly had a man's mind.

Miss Reid: Did she really?

Doctor: She also very nearly had a man's moustache.

He gives Miss Reid a charming smile and rises. Miss

74

Reid turns in slight consternation to Mrs. Robinson and starts a conversation as the doctor moves away.

31. *Exterior upper deck. Day. The doctor, proceeding along the deck, rounds a corner and meets the captain going in the opposite direction.*

CAPTAIN: Where are you going?

DOCTOR: I'm escaping!

CAPTAIN: Miss Reid?

The doctor nods and the Captain turns and moves off with the doctor.

DISSOLVE

32. *Montage. A short sequence now follows showing the terrible effect Miss Reid has on the other passengers and on the officers. Here and there, all over the ship, groups of people—officers and passengers—are seen talking together when round the corner from them comes the sound of Miss Reid's incessant chatter. They flee from her, leaving the deck completely empty. Eventually it appears that the vessel is haunted by the sound of her voice: short cuts of companionways, the upper deck, the lounge, the dining saloon, et cetera, but always that interminable cliché-ridden questioning. The ship's siren is the only sound that will drown the noise out.*

33. *Exterior ocean. Day (stock shot). The ship, siren sounding, is approaching Jamaica.*

DISSOLVE

34. *Exterior Kingston quayside. Day (stock shot). The vessel is lying alongside, unloading cargo.*

35. *Exterior Kingston quayside. Day. Disembarkation of passengers. Miss Reid, prominent, laughing and chatting and pointing around with her sunshade as she goes off for a couple of hours' shopping.*

DISSOLVE

36. *Exterior ship's deck. Day. The doctor is leaning over the rail. He is joined by the chief engineer.*

ENGINEER: Well, Doc? They've gone—every blessed one of them!

75

DOCTOR: Yes—for the time being!

ENGINEER: What's that mean?

DOCTOR: Our Friend, Miss Reid, is still with us.

ENGINEER (*wryly*): Mmm! Well, we'll be picking up new passengers at Trinidad.

DOCTOR: Poor souls! So happy in Trinidad—so soon to be drowned in a sea of chatter!

ENGINEER: Where *is* she—Miss Reid?

DOCTOR: Gone off into the town. To buy herself a lot of junk, no doubt.

ENGINEER: I must say it's a pleasure for a moment not to have to listen to that voice.

Miss Reid's voice is heard.

MISS REID'S VOICE (*gaily*): Hello, there!

DOCTOR (*quietly*): You spoke too soon!

Miss Reid, laden with parcels, joins them.

MISS REID: I've had such a lovely idea. Tomorrow I'm going to ask for a picnic basket and I'm going to snatch you men away from dull old routine for a little jaunt.

DOCTOR: I'm afraid . . .

MISS REID: No excuses! I'm quite determined.

The Captain joins them, frowning.

ENGINEER: Anything wrong, Tom?

CAPTAIN: I've just been to see the agent. We've been ordered straight back to England. The passengers we were picking up at Trinidad are being accommodated on another ship.

MISS REID: Oh, but how very disappointing—I was so looking forward to visiting Trinidad.

CAPTAIN (*seizing his opportunity*): Naturally, Miss Reid. Well, I tell you what we'll do. I can easily arrange for you to be transferred to another ship.

MISS REID (*after a moment's thought*): That's awfully nice of you, Captain, but d'you know, I think I'd really rather stay with you. Already I'm beginning to feel this ship has become my home.

CAPTAIN: You realize there won't be any other passengers on the ship, Miss Reid?

MISS REID (*puzzled*): I don't think I—— Oh, you mean I'll be alone with all you men. Oh well, never mind. I always say that if a lady's a lady, a gentleman will be a gentleman. I'm sure it will be most amusing. (*Going—cheerfully*) I'll be seeing you all later then!

The three men stare at each other.

CAPTAIN: Alone wi' yon woman!

ENGINEER: For all of fourteen days!

DOCTOR: Nothing to be heard but the sea and the wind and Miss Reid! (*He takes a resolute breath.*) I shall take either to my bed or to the bottle. Possibly both!

DISSOLVE

37. *Exterior Kingston quayside. Day. Loading of cargo being completed. General bustle.*

DISSOLVE

38. *Exterior Jamaica Harbour. Day (stock shot). The ship is moving slowly out of the harbour.*

39. *Ship on the high seas (stock shot).*

40. *General shot of ship under way. Day (studio or stock).*

41. *Exterior bridge. Day. The Captain is on the bridge singing, apparently cheerfully.*

42. *Exterior section of upper deck. Day. As Miss Reid comes along the deck beneath the bridge, she hears the Captain singing and pauses for a moment to enjoy his indistinct rendering of a song.*

43. *Exterior bridge. Day. Medium close shot of the Captain. He is working hard at something and is quite unconscious of the words he is singing to the tune of "Auld Lang Syne," as he has been singing them over and over for some time.*

CAPTAIN (*singing*):

> Miss Reid, you are a dreadful bore,
> You don't appeal to me.
> I'd like to pick you up, Miss Reid
> And throw you in the sea.
> And throw you in the sea, Miss Reid,
> It really would be fine,
> To throw you in the sea, Miss Reid,
> For the sake of Auld Lang Syne.

77

44. *Exterior section of upper deck. Day. Miss Reid, beneath the bridge, delighted at the Captain's cheerfulness, smiles and continues on her way along the deck. Thinking she is joining his mood, she hums happily to herself. She goes out of picture.*

45. *Exterior upper deck. Day. Miss Reid moves into picture and arrives in front of the doctor. He has closed his eyes at her approach.*

MISS REID (*troubled*): Doctor! You look dreadfully ill.

DOCTOR: I'm in pain.

MISS REID: I know—I can see that. Can't something be done?

DOCTOR: No. It'll pass off presently.

MISS REID: I really feel I ought to do something.

He closes his eyes. Miss Reid looks at him for a second, then goes to her nearby chair, where her knitting, rug and cushions, et cetera, are lying, the camera panning with her. She picks up a small pillow and crosses back to the doctor with it.

MISS REID: You look so uncomfortable with no cushions or anything. Let me put my pillow behind your head.

The doctor feels too ill to remonstrate as Miss Reid lifts up his head and places the soft pillow behind it. The camera tracks in a little.

MISS REID: There! Is that better? (*Not waiting for a reply*) Poor dear! I know what doctors are—they haven't got the first idea how to take care of themselves. Now, I'm not going to let you talk; I'm just going to sit beside you and knit. I always think it's a comfort when one isn't feeling well to have someone near.

During this, Miss Reid has sat down and now busily begins to knit.

DISSOLVE

46. *Exterior upper deck. Day. A sailor is proceeding along the deck. As he approaches the chairs on which Miss Reid and the doctor are sitting, Miss Reid puts down her book and knitting and puts a finger to her lips. (She is the kind of accomplished knitter who can read a book at the same time.) The sailor passes by. The doctor suddenly opens his eyes.*

78

DOCTOR: Hullo.

MISS REID: You've slept for over an hour. How's the pain?

DOCTOR: Gone.

They exchange a smile.

MISS REID: D'you feel strong enough to come and eat something?

DOCTOR (*getting up*): Yes—yes, I think I do.

47. *Miss Reid puts aside her knitting and her book and stands up beside the doctor. Together they walk along the deck, the camera tracking with them.*

MISS REID (*brightly*): Are you fond of reading, Doctor?

DOCTOR: Yes.

MISS REID: So am I. The moment I saw you I thought you looked clever.

The doctor gives her a brief look but says nothing.

MISS REID: Of course one can always read. I prefer a good talk to a good book. Don't you?

DOCTOR: No.

MISS REID: How very interesting. Now do tell me why.

DOCTOR: I can't give you a reason.

MISS REID: That's very strange, isn't it? But than I always think human nature is strange.

It occurs to the doctor that Miss Reid is fairly strange herself, and he shoots her a look half amused, half exasperated.

DOCTOR: It was very kind of you to bother about me, Miss Reid. Thank you.

MISS REID: It was nothing at all! I can't bear to see anyone suffering—or any *thing*, for that matter. D'you know, it quite upsets me even to see a tree being cut down.

DOCTOR (*gravely*): You must lead a very emotional life.

The camera now finishes tracking and pans them into a medium long shot as they cross towards the lounge.

48. *Interior lounge. Day. The Captain, the mate and the chief engineer are standing in a group. Pierre is serving pink gins. The engineer refuses.*

CAPTAIN: Och, come on, man! You'll need something to get you through the meal with Delilah!

The Captain is slightly taken aback by the appearance of Miss Reid and the doctor.

Miss Reid: Now, now! No ceremony! I want to be treated as if I were simply a member of the crew. Just talk away as though I weren't here at all. (*Seeing the drinks*) What are those?

Captain: Pink gins.

Miss Reid (*to Pierre*): I'll have one. I always think it's such a nice, clean drink.

Doctor: A nice, clean, *strong* drink.

Miss Reid: Oh? Do you find it strong? How interesting. (*To engineer*) The pink part comes from the East Indies, doesn't it, Mr. Andrews?

The chief engineer fingers his collar nervously.

Engineer: Er . . .

Miss Reid: Now, come along! You've been in the East Indies, I know. Tell us about it! (*To Captain*) I intend to draw you all out. I mean to find out all about each one of you! It's the thing I think is so . . . (*Pierre gives her her drink.*) Thank you! . . . So interesting about the sea. (*She drinks about half the drink.*) The restriction—people are thrown back upon themselves. Like the Brontës. (*She finishes the gin and smiles at the engineer.*) You know what I mean?

The chief engineer gives Miss Reid a dazed and completely uncomprehending smile.

Miss Reid: Don't you agree with me, Doctor? Steward, we'll all have one more. (*As they are about to protest*) Yes! This round's on me. (*To doctor*) The sea, as I was saying, makes people fall back upon one another.

Doctor: So do pink gins!

Miss Reid (*smiling*): Ah! (*Seriously*) But you know what I mean? The restricted space—all living together—it forces people to make their own entertainment—like the Brontës. Now I don't know which of us is Charlotte. But I know which of us is Emily—you, with your quiet, detached, *clever* mind—you, Doctor, I should say, are *Emily*.

The doctor raises one eyebrow and exchanges a glance with the Captain. The chief engineer, increasingly dazed, looks from Miss Reid to the doctor.

Miss Reid: Yes, definitely Emily!

Miss Reid continues with perfect self-satisfaction.

Miss Reid: What fun all this is! (*To Captain*) There's

so much I want to know about the ship. I've thousands of questions up my sleeve for you. Nothing around us but sea and sky, and yet, there we shall be, back in England in thirteen days.

Pierre returns to serve the drinks, and Miss Reid's attention is distracted.

CAPTAIN (*quietly*): Thirteen days! Thirteen days! (*and, in one gulp, finishes his drink*).

MISS REID (*turning*): What was that?

CAPTAIN: Oh—just a technical matter!

MISS REID: But technical matters are just the thing I'm itching to know about. Tell me . . .

CAPTAIN: It would bore you.

MISS REID (*gravely*): I'm never bored. That's why, if you won't think me conceited for saying so, that's why I'm never boring.

The Captain, about to take a second pink gin from Pierre, is so startled that he knocks over his glass.

CAPTAIN: Oh!

MISS REID (*smiling*): *That's* right! (*Delighted*) Just swear away as though I weren't here at all! (*Turning from him*) Doctor! I've got simply heaps of questions I want to ask *you*. For instance . . .

DOCTOR: Delighted, but . . . (*To Captain*) I think I just ought to go and take some more medicine.

He moves away towards the door.

CAPTAIN (*following him*): But . . .

DOCTOR (*nearing the door and giving the Captain his gin*): Perhaps you'll be kind enough to drink that for me?

CAPTAIN (*grimly*): Thanks—Emily!

The doctor turns and goes out of the lounge. At the same time the gong for the meal sounds.

49. *Exterior and interior ship's lounge. Day. Camera shooting into the lounge through the door from out on deck. As the doctor comes out, the rest of the party can be seen in the background moving down the stairs to the dining saloon on the lower deck.*

MISS REID (*moving in on him*): Now, tell me, Captain . . .

The doctor steps out onto the deck, closes the door and heaves a sigh of relief.

50. *Interior doctor's cabin. Day. The doctor is sitting con-*
tentedly reading, munching some biscuits, with a whisky
and soda beside him. Suddenly the sound of Miss Reid's
voice is heard approaching along the deck. It grows louder.

MISS REID (*off*): . . . but if you don't mind my saying
so . . .

The doctor looks up with apprehension.

MISS REID (*off*): . . . I do think you ought to do something about the curtains in the saloon. (*Her voice begins*
to decrease in volume as she passes.) I'm sure something
brighter would be much prettier . . .

The door opens suddenly and the Captain appears for a
second.

CAPTAIN (*to the doctor*): Rat!

The Captain closes the door.

CAPTAIN (*from the deck—off*): What was that, Miss
Reid?

The doctor, with a broad smile, continues his biscuits
and his drink.

51. *Interior Captain's cabin. Night. The Captain, the chief*
engineer and the mate are sitting talking. The doctor
enters.

CAPTAIN: Come in, Doctor. We're having a council of
war about yon woman.

CAPTAIN (*to doctor*): We were wondering how we're
going to have a real good Christmas Eve party wi' her
among us.

ENGINEER: For once, couldn't we just ignore her?

CAPTAIN: Man, ye canna ignore Niagara.

MATE (*morosely*): D'you know what she is? She's a
human long-playing record.

CAPTAIN: Well, I wish somebody would take her off.

DOCTOR: I wish somebody would take her *on*.

CAPTAIN: D'you mean—for better or worse?

DOCTOR: Yes! Some nice, young single man. Like Joe!

MATE (*half rising*): 'Ere! I'm going.

CAPTAIN: Sit down, Joe. (*To doctor*) Are you serious?

DOCTOR: As a doctor, I'd say that all Miss Reid needs

is—how shall I put it lightly, so as not to shock Joe—all she needs is . . . romance.

CAPTAIN: (*stunned*): Romance?

DOCTOR (*blithely*): Yes! Involve Miss Reid in a romance —and we should have peace and quiet.

CAPTAIN: We'd have *quiet?* You're sure?

DOCTOR: Certain!

CAPTAIN: Then all we have to do is find the man.

The Captain and the doctor fix Joe with a look. Joe looks from one to the other and nervously fingers his collar.

JOE (*heatedly*): It's—it's no use looking at me. I've got a young lady in Tilbury.

DOCTOR: Oh! Well, then, Captain? How about you?

CAPTAIN: Och, away! I'm no' romantic—and I don't want to lose my wife after all these years.

DOCTOR: A little light romance with Miss Reid? Your wife wouldn't leave you because of that.

CAPTAIN: I was no' thinking I'd lose my wife because she'd leave me. I was thinking I'd lose her because she'd die laughing.

MATE: How about you, Doctor?

CAPTAIN: Aye! It's your diagnosis.

DOCTOR: It's my professional duty to prescribe remedies, but it's not part of my professional duty to administer the remedies in person.

CAPTAIN: Well, I'll no' put up wi' another ten days of her blether. A man has got to be found!

He looks up and his eyes happen to meet the chief engineer's.

ENGINEER (*hotly*): The answer, gentlemen, is in the negative.

At the same time Pierre has entered, bringing a syphon of soda water. The Captain suddenly looks at him.

CAPTAIN: We've got to find . . .

As the Captain stares at Pierre, the doctor, the chief engineer and the mate follow his glance.

CAPTAIN: Pierre, are you married?

PIERRE: No, sir.

CAPTAIN: Engaged?

PIERRE: No, sir.

The four officers exchange glances.

CAPTAIN: Ye know we have a lady on board?

PIERRE: Yes, sir?

DOCTOR: A very charming lady. (*Pierre does not answer.*) A very—*delightful* lady!

CAPTAIN (*to Pierre*): Well?

PIERRE (*with a little shrug and a charming smile*): All ladies are delightful, sir.

CAPTAIN: Ah! That's my boy! (*To doctor*) The real romantic style! (*To Pierre*) Well now, ye know, although we're a cargo ship, the Company's anxious to encourage the passenger side of the line.

PIERRE: Yes, sir?

CAPTAIN: And I've instructions to promote the happiness of those sailing in our ships. And I think—we think——

DOCTOR: We felt that if Miss Reid were to find herself . . . caught up in a romance, it would be very nice!

PIERRE (*pleasantly*): Very nice! (*They all relax, delighted.*) Very unlikely, but very nice!

CAPTAIN: Why unlikely?

PIERRE: Well . . . for romance is necessary a certain warmth . . .

DOCTOR: That nonsense about Englishwomen being icebergs is just a fallacy made up by the French.

PIERRE: Yes, sir.

CAPTAIN: Ye're no' all that busy on this ship, and to cut the cackle, I've selected you to provide the romance.

Pierre looks blankly astonished.

PIERRE: M-me, sir? But . . . (*at a loss for an excuse*) . . . but I have all the washing up and—and . . .

CAPTAIN: Ye'll have to work in your romance wi' your washing up, like thousands of others have . . .

PIERRE: But, sir—I am not romantic. I am—I am . . . *timid*.

CAPTAIN: Timid? You? A Frenchman?

PIERRE: We are not all great lovers. This is a fallacy about the French, made up by the English.

The Doctor laughs.

DOCTOR: Miss Reid is a lady of the highest distinction. If she were French she'd be at least a countess.

PIERRE: But even so, I don't quite see why she must suddenly be provided with romance—in the middle of the sea?

CAPTAIN: The middle of the sea's as good as any other place.

DOCTOR (*explaining to Pierre, with gravity*): It is customary on Christmas Eve for English ladies of exalted rank to be involved in light romance.

PIERRE (*blankly*): Oh?

CAPTAIN: Besides, this would be a chance to improve your English, and it's no' often you can combine entertainment wi' intellectual improvement. You're a very fortunate young man!

PIERRE (*suddenly resolute*): Sir! I'm sorry, but . . .

CAPTAIN (*blazing at him*): It's no' a request I'm making. You will present yourself to Miss Reid!

PIERRE: When?

CAPTAIN: I don't know. After dinner.

PIERRE: But what shall I do?

CAPTAIN: Do? Act naturally! That's an *order!*

Pierre looks bewildered, but has sprung to attention at the Captain's tone of command.

MATE (*going back on duty, whispering in Pierre's ear*): Cheer up. You'll get danger money.

DISSOLVE

52. *Interior ship's lounge. Night. The Captain, the doctor, the chief engineer and Miss Reid are coming up into the lounge. They sit at a table in the corner. Pierre crosses to them, serving coffee.*

MISS REID: What a delicious dinner!

The Captain is lost in thought, studying Pierre. Pierre catches the Captain's eye on him and, overcome with sudden nerves, nearly drops a coffee cup. He saves it and hurries away.

MISS REID: A penny for your thoughts, Captain.

CAPTAIN (*with a slight twinkle in his eye*): Oh—they're worth more than a penny.

MISS REID: And what are *we* thinking about, Doctor? Hardly a word out of us since the soup; we mustn't get broody, you know. (*Getting up*) I believe I'm going to take my coffee out on deck. There's nothing I like more than to stand and look at the sky. I adore that *vast*—silence!

During this, she has crossed to the door, the camera panning with her. She goes out on deck.

85

CAPTAIN (*thunderstruck*): She adores that vast—silence!

DOCTOR (*quietly*): She's a perfect example of someone killing the thing they love.

Both are left looking after her.

53. *Close shot of the Captain to cover.*

54. *Medium close shot of Pierre to cover.*

55. *Medium close shot of Miss Reid to cover.*

56. *Two shot of the Captain and the doctor to cover.*

57. *Exterior upper deck. Night. Miss Reid is standing gazing at the sky.*

58. *Interior ship's lounge. Night. The Captain looks at Pierre and jerks his head towards the door through which Miss Reid has gone. Pierre gives the Captain an anguished look and goes.*

59. *Interior ship's lounge. Night. The Captain is lighting a cigar.*

CAPTAIN: I've never had much faith in you doctors, as you know. But, my word, if you manage to stem that tide of conversation . . .

DOCTOR: Think of tomorrow! That vast silence!

DISSOLVE

60. *Interior Dining Saloon. Day. The whole party is at lunch; Miss Reid is talking more loudly and faster than ever. The Captain and the doctor are sunk in gloom.*

MISS REID: . . . it's just a matter of being firm. Go to the Head Office and say: "You've just *got* to take away those drab old curtains." I know I can be very persistent, and I shall just go on nagging about those curtains no matter how much you want to pick me up and throw me in the sea.

The Captain, who is sipping water, chokes suddenly.

MISS REID (*continuing*): Doctor! Don't you agree with me? Environment is the remedy for so many ills.

CAPTAIN: Don't ask the doctor about remedies. It's a subject he knows nothing about!

Pierre is removing plates.

86

Miss Reid: Oh, come now! That's like saying you don't know how to steer the ship, or whatever it is you get up to on the bridge.

Pierre goes.

Miss Reid (*quietly*): Oh, do you know, I had such a funny experience last night; with the steward.

The Captain and the doctor sit up with a jerk.

Doctor: With the steward?

Miss Reid: I was just retiring to rest, when there was a knock at my door. "Who is it?" I said. "It's the steward, madame," he answered. "Can I speak to you?" I popped on a dressing gown and opened the door and said "Yes?" "Excuse me, madame," he said, "but I wondered if you'd like a nice cup of tea?"

Miss Reid laughs. The Captain and the doctor exchange a glance.

Captain: Was that all he said?

Miss Reid: Yes! I nearly laughed—it appealed to my sense of humour, if you know what I mean. But I didn't want to hurt his feelings, so I just said, "No, thank you," wished him good night and pleasant dreams, and shut the door.

Miss Reid has risen during the latter part of this speech and crosses to the doorway.

Captain: The—the idiot!

Miss Reid (*turning*): Oh *no!* I know just what it was. He's young and French, and he's got that idea that English people drink tea at all times, so he just wanted to—give me a treat.

Captain: I shall . . .

Miss Reid: Now, you're not to be cross with him—I didn't mind at all. I like these queer little things that happen to one when one's travelling. I just get a good laugh out of them.

Captain: Steward!

Pierre comes into the saloon through the glass doors from the passage. He is slightly embarrassed at finding himself face to face with Miss Reid and politely makes way for her to go out on deck. He closes the door after her.

Pierre: Sir?

Captain: What in the . . . (*He bangs the table.*) For

heaven's sake, man—what possessed you last night to ask Miss Reid if she wanted a cup of tea?

PIERRE: I am a steward, sir. You told me to act naturally. I thought it was the natural thing to do . . .

CAPTAIN: Now, I'll not have any more filly-fally. (*He bangs the table again.*) Romance the lady needs—romance the lady's going to get!

DISSOLVE

61. *Interior Miss Reid's cabin. Night. Miss Reid is sitting at her dressing table. She is busily trying to fix a curler into her hair. There is a knock.*

MISS REID: Who is it?

PIERRE: The steward.

MISS REID (*calling*): I didn't ring.

There is no answer. Miss Reid rises and crosses towards the door.

MISS REID: Hullo?

PIERRE (*off*): Yes, madame?

MISS REID: I didn't ring. (*There is no answer.*) Je . . . er . . . je n'ai pas sonne.

PIERRE: I have a radio message for you, Miss Reid.

MISS REID (*startled*): A radio message? (*She relaxes.*) Oh, it'll be a Christmas greeting from Miss Price, I expect. How very kind.

PIERRE: I have a radio message for you, Miss Reid.

MISS REID: I was just . . . er . . . (*She is about to open the door, when she realizes she has the curler hanging in her hair. She tugs at it, but cannot loosen it.*) Er—would you leave it outside the door?

She moves away a step.

PIERRE: It's prepaid. It must have an answer.

MISS REID (*alarmed*): An answer? Then it can't be from . . . (*Returning to the door, tugging at the curler*) Oh dear! I hope it's not bad news. (*Still unsuccessful with the curler*) Would you—would you slip it under the door?

The radio message appears under the door. Miss Reid picks it up with some disquiet and opens it.

MISS REID (*to herself*): Where did I put my specs? What a silly-billy! (*She finds them, puts them on and reads.*)

62. *Insert: Close shot of the message. It reads*: "*Happy Christmas Stop Peace and good will to all men stop How you are beautiful Stop I love you Stop I must speak with you Stop Steward.*"

63. *Interior Miss Reid's cabin. Night. Removing her glasses, Miss Reid takes in the message. Absent-mindedly, but with dexterity, she removes the curler from her hair, puts down her glasses, and goes and opens the door. Miss Reid and Pierre look at one another for a second.*

MISS REID (*pleasantly*): Come in.

Pierre enters. Miss Reid turns to him, and Pierre tries to think of something to say. There is a slight pause.

PIERRE (*inspired*): Bon soir.

MISS REID: Bon soir. Won't you sit down?

PIERRE: Oh, but I should not . . .

MISS REID: Let's be unconventional.

PIERRE (*puzzled*): Un . . . ?

MISS REID: It means, let's be—er—*bohème*. Well, no. Perhaps not exactly *bohème*. Anyway—*asseyez-vous*.

PIERRE: I'm afraid it is lousy—my English.

MISS REID: Oh! You mustn't say that.

PIERRE: What? English?

MISS REID: No. The—other word. Yes, I'm afraid your English isn't of the best. That's really why I thought we ought to have a little talk.

PIERRE: Yes?

MISS REID (*smiling kindly*): I know *why* you wrote me that message.

PIERRE: You know?

MISS REID: You said to yourself, "Here's Miss Reid, all alone, with Christmas Eve in the offing, so I'll send her a little message to cheer her up."

PIERRE: Er . . .

MISS REID (*patting his shoulder*): And it's a very *nice* little message.

PIERRE (*puzzled*): Nice?

MISS REID: But—and you won't mind my saying this— but because of language difficulties, your message is not quite correct.

PIERRE: I didn't think it *was* (*with a slight shrug and a faint smile*)—correct.

89

Miss Reid: What a nuisance these old languages are, aren't they? Well, now, your message is very nice, but you haven't said what you wanted to say.

Pierre: No?

Miss Reid (*looking at the message*): "Happy Christmas." That's perfectly correct. "Peace and good will to all men." Excellent! "How you are beautiful." No.

Pierre: No?

Miss Reid: There you're in difficulties with your French verb "*aimer*," which, as you know, can be used to mean "I like you" or "I love you." What you meant was: "I like you."

Pierre: No.

There is a slight pause.

Miss Reid: I beg your pardon?

Pierre: No.

Slight pause.

Miss Reid: Well—what *did* you mean?

Pierre: What I said.

There is a pause.

Pierre (*shyly*): Would you like a little walk round the deck?

Pierre goes and opens the door with a flourish.

Pierre (*smiling*): *La vie est belle.* Life is *nice*. Correct?

Miss Reid (*shaking her head, absent-mindedly*): Beautiful. Life is beautiful. (*She passes him.*) And very extraordinary!

Miss Reid and Pierre move out into the corridor and across to the companionway.

64. *Upper deck. Night. Miss Reid and Pierre are seen walking away from camera along the deck.*

FADE OUT

FADE IN

65. *Interior Dining Saloon. Day. Luncheon is being served. Silence reigns. The chief engineer and the mate are eating steadily. The mate looks across at the doctor, who is eating with downcast eyes. The Captain looks fussed. Miss Reid is eating calmly. All the officers are obviously very constrained and embarrassed by having achieved the*

"quiet" they desired. After a while the Captain can bear it no more and he breaks the silence.

CAPTAIN: You're very quiet today, Miss Reid.

MISS REID (*calmly*): I'm thinking.

DOCTOR (*trying "charm"*): And won't you tell us your thoughts, Miss Reid?

Miss Reid gives him a cool look.

MISS REID: I prefer to keep them to myself, Doctor.

With this shattering remark, Miss Reid creates another very awkward silence, but the Captain is not to be put down.

CAPTAIN (*brightly—turning to Miss Reid*): Have you ever been to Ceylon?

Miss Reid merely shakes her head negatively. There is another slight pause.

CAPTAIN (*to doctor*): Have *you* ever been to Ceylon?

DOCTOR (*with false social interest*): Yes, I once saw a native production of *Julius Caesar* in Ceylon.

CAPTAIN (*too brightly*): That must have been rather interesting.

DOCTOR (*suddenly depressed*): As a matter of fact, it was quite idiotic.

There is another pause. Pierre approaches.

PIERRE: Will you take coffee, madame?

MISS REID (*with her usual calm, pleasant smile*): No, thank you.

At the same time as Pierre moves away, Miss Reid prepares to get up.

CAPTAIN: Nice-looking young chap, Pierre.

MISS REID (*placidly*): Who?

CAPTAIN: The steward.

MISS REID: Is he? I suppose so. I hadn't really thought about it.

With this, Miss Reid moves out of the Dining Saloon, leaving the ships officers thoroughly disconcerted. As the men resettle themselves, the Captain catches Pierre's eye. The Captain jerks his head silently for Pierre to approach. Pierre comes across.

CAPTAIN (*suddenly, not quite knowing how to begin*): Er—well?

PIERRE: Sir?

CAPTAIN: Have you—er—anything to tell us?

91

PIERRE (*apparently quite at a loss*): About what, sir?
The Captain, enraged, thumps the table.
CAPTAIN: You know very well about what!
PIERRE: If it—if it's about Miss Reid, sir . . .
CAPTAIN: Go on!
PIERRE: You told me she was a lady of exalted rank.
Surely it is not customary among British gentlemen to discuss such a lady behind her back, sir?
The Captain fidgets about, a prey to nervous exasperation.
CAPTAIN: Er—yes. No! (*He sees a smile on the doctor's face.*) What are you grinning at? (*Irritably to Pierre*) Oh, it doesn't matter. Go away!
Pierre retreats, with the faintest suspicion of a smile on his lips.

DISSOLVE

66. *Interior ship's lounge. Night. The Christmas party is in progress. Everyone is present, with the exception of Miss Reid.*
DOCTOR (*to Captain*): Anything worrying you, Captain?
CAPTAIN: No, no! I just—— (*To steward*) Where's Miss Reid?
PIERRE: Sitting out on deck, sir.
CAPTAIN: Does she know the party's started?
PIERRE: I think so, sir.
CAPTAIN (*to Pierre*): Well, then—go and ask Miss Reid if she'll not give us the pleasure of her company.
Pierre goes.

67. *Exterior upper deck. Night. Miss Reid is sitting calmly in the moonlight. Pierre approaches.*
PIERRE: The Captain's compliments, Miss Reid, and won't you join him in the lounge?
Miss Reid smiles noncommittally at him.
MISS REID: Very well! If he really insists.
She gives a little sigh and rises.

68. *Interior ship's lounge. Night.*
CAPTAIN (*talking to men*): . . . Glasgow may belong to you, I said, but this happens to be Edinburgh and those happen to be my feet you're standing on. (*Seeing Miss*

92

Reid coming in) Ah, Miss Reid! There you are! (*Going to her and bringing her in*) Now, come along in and have a wee drink. (*Leading her to the bar*) What'll it be? Will it be champagne, or will it be something a bit milder?

MISS REID (*after a moment's thought*): Champagne!

DISSOLVE

69. *Interior ship's lounge. Night. General shot of the party, getting much gayer. A radio officer is playing the piano. The Captain, the doctor and Miss Reid are relaxing round the piano, laughing and talking. The pianist starts to play "Lily of Laguna" (a Christmas carol) and Miss Reid picks up the tune. Surprisingly she has a young, fresh and charming voice and, in a moment, has swept them all into the song with her. As the singing gets louder and louder . . .*

FADE OUT

70. *Exterior upper deck. Day. Miss Reid is standing by the rail, throwing bread to the gulls. The doctor approaches.*
DOCTOR: Coming in to breakfast, Miss Reid?
MISS REID: I've had mine already, thank you, Doctor.
She turns away and the doctor is left speechless, to wander off by himself.

71. *Interior Dining Saloon. Day. The Captain is sitting at the table. He picks up a parcel.*
CAPTAIN: What's this?
PIERRE: From Miss Reid, sir.
The Captain starts to undo it.
CAPTAIN: Tell the chef I want my coffee black and strong.
The chief engineer and the mate have entered.
CAPTAIN (*indicating parcels*): They're from Miss Reid.
MATE (*as he and the chief engineer pick up and unwrap their parcels*): What are they?
CAPTAIN (*who has unwrapped his parcel and finds a pipe*): Presents, you idiot!
MATE (*awkwardly*): She oughtn't to have given us presents.
CHIEF ENGINEER: Silk handkerchiefs!
MATE: This is a smashin' tie!
The doctor has entered.

93

CAPTAIN (*to doctor*): There's a present for you too—from Miss Reid.

ENGINEER: Makes me feel a bit—a bit . . .

CAPTAIN: Me too!

DOCTOR: Cigars!

CAPTAIN: Well, come on, I think we'd better go and thank her. Come on!

72. *Exterior upper deck. Day. Miss Reid is still standing at the rail, throwing bread. The Captain approaches, and the rest follow slightly sheepishly behind.*

CAPTAIN: Miss Reid! I—er—I'm sure we don't know how to thank you for your kind thought.

ENGINEER (*through the end of the Captain's speech*): I don't know why you should have. We—er—we didn't expect . . .

MATE: ⎱ It was awfully . . .
DOCTOR: ⎰ We ought to have . . .

The mate and the doctor grin feebly at each other.

MISS REID: Oh, it's nothing. You've all been so very kind to me. I'm afraid there wasn't a great selection in Kingston.

DOCTOR: We appreciate it very much.

There is a slight embarrassed silence.

ENGINEER: Miss Reid, I—I wonder if you'd care to come down and look at the engine room after breakfast? I'd be glad to show it to you.

MISS REID: That *is* nice of you. I'd like to very much, but . . .

ENGINEER: Any time you like. (*Retreating*) And—and thanks again—very much.

MATE: Just say the word when you want to go down, Miss Reid. Be pleased to show you the way. And—thanks ever so much for the tie. Awfully kind of you.

He retreats awkwardly.

DOCTOR: I feel most thoughtless not to have got something for you.

CAPTAIN: Yes indeed!

The Captain awkwardly makes an excuse to go up to the bridge, and the doctor unhappily walks away in the opposite direction. Miss Reid is left alone, silently feeding the gulls.

FADE OUT

73. *Exterior mouth of Thames. Day. (Location.) The vessel is moving up the river.*

74. *Interior Miss Reid's cabin. Day. Miss Reid is packing; humming to herself as she works, she finds the curlers. She looks at them and, with a half-smile, packs them in her bag.*

75. *Exterior English quayside. Day. (Location.) The vessel docking.*

DISSOLVE

76. *Exterior Interior English quayside (shed). Day. Shooting from the shed on to the ship's gangway. People are already coming down the gangway.*

77. *Exterior ship's deck and gangway. Day. The ship is lying alongside at West India Dock. The doctor and the Captain are standing at the head of the gangway. Miss Reid, all ready to disembark, joins them.*

MISS REID: I just wanted to say how much I've appreciated your kindness—both of you.

CAPTAIN: } Och, it's been . . .
DOCTOR: } Please don't . . .

MISS REID: No, really! You've been wonderful. You've thought of everything. Everything. . . . (*They look modestly pleased.*) . . . even romance! (*The Captain and the doctor are immensely startled. They look at her.*)

CAPTAIN: W-what?

MISS REID (*smiling*): Now don't deny it! (*Pleasantly enjoying herself*) I'm not a complete idiot, you know. When a good-looking young man appears and tells me he's in love with me, something tells me there's something fishy going on.

CAPTAIN: } Oh, but . . .
DOCTOR: } I'm sure you . . .

MISS REID: I try to make the best of myself, but I'm perfectly aware that I'm not a young man's dream of bliss! But thank you so much for thinking of it. It was a charming idea.

CAPTAIN (*overcome with shame*): Miss Reid, I feel I owe you an apology.

DOCTOR: It was really my fault . . .

Miss Reid (*gaily*): But there's nothing to apologize for. I was highly amused. And, after all, who knows—your idea *might* have been a success.

The two men stare at one another as Miss Reid looks down at the dockside and, seeing Miss Price, waves to her.

78. *Exterior English quayside (shed). Day. Miss Price in the shed is standing waiting. She catches sight of Miss Reid and moves to the end of the gangway.*

79. *Exterior ship's deck and gangway. Day. Crane shot. Miss Reid is about to step onto the gangway.*

Miss Reid: Good-bye, Captain. Good-bye, Doctor.

Doctor: Good-bye, Miss Reid, and . . . (*quietly*) I hope you've forgiven me?

Captain: And I hope you'll forgive me too, Miss Reid. I'm afraid I underestimated your common sense.

Miss Reid (*as she continues on down the gangway—not giving anything away*): Good-bye, Captain.

The camera cranes down with her as she goes down the gangway to the dockside. Miss Price, waiting at the bottom of the gangway, comes into picture.

Miss Reid: Nora! How *nice* of you! How *are* you?

80. *Exterior ship's deck and gangway. Day. The Captain and the doctor are looking down at the quay.*

Captain: She was a real sport.

81. *Exterior Interior English quayside (shed). Day. Miss Reid and Miss Price are walking away from the ship. Camera cranes with them.*

Miss Reid (*stopping*): Oh, I must just wave.

Miss Reid turns back.

82. *Exterior Ship's deck and gangway. Day. The Captain and doctor looking down.*

Captain: Look, she's waving.

Doctor: Yes, but not at us.

The doctor and the Captain wave back, then realize Miss Reid is not waving to them. Together they bend over the side of the ship to see who it is.

83. *Exterior lower part of ship. Day. Pierre is waving through a porthole to Miss Reid.*

84. *Exterior Interior English quayside (shed). Day (Resume 81). Crane shot. Miss Reid is waving to Pierre. She smiles, gives one final wave, then turns back to Miss Price.*

MISS PRICE (*looking up*): Such a nice ship.

Miss Reid blows her nose vigorously.

MISS REID (*briskly*): Well—while we're waiting for the luggage, how about some tea?

Miss Price turns to her, and they set off. The camera pulls back and all the dockside traffic (luggage, crates, et cetera) crosses between them and the camera.

DISSOLVE

85. *Interior Teashop. Day (Moving matte). Miss Price and Miss Reid are having tea.*

MISS REID: . . . but I always say one has to take things as they come.

MISS PRICE: What sort of things do you mean?

MISS REID: Just funny, unexpected, rather nice things. There is no doubt that travel definitely broadens the mind.

MISS PRICE: Oh, it does all sound such fun. How I wish I could go on a cruise. But my brother says it's a waste of money.

MISS REID: Why don't you just tell your brother you've been ordered to go—by the doctor?

MISS PRICE (*doubtfully*): Yes. But would he believe me?

MISS REID (*smiling faintly*): My dear, if one puts one's mind to it, one can make men believe anything.

MISS PRICE: What are you smiling at?

MISS REID: Oh—nothing very much.

MISS PRICE: I expect you'll be quite glad to get back to "Molly's Parlour"?

MISS REID: Do you know, I think I'm going to change the name. I'm rather tired of "Molly's Parlour." I thought I'd change it to . . . "Chez Molly."

MISS PRICE: "Chez Molly." French.

MISS REID: Yes. (*She raises a hand.*) Miss!

FADE OUT

THE END

GIGOLO AND GIGOLETTE

THE bar was crowded. Sandy Westcott had had a couple of cocktails, and he was beginning to feel hungry. He looked at his watch. He had been asked to dinner at half-past nine, and it was nearly ten. Eva Barrett was always late, and he would be lucky if he got anything to eat by ten-thirty. He turned to the barman to order another cocktail and caught sight of a man who at that moment came up to the bar.

"Hullo, Cotman," he said. "Have a drink."

"I don't mind if I do, sir."

Cotman was a nice-looking fellow, of thirty perhaps, short, but with so good a figure that he did not look it, very smartly dressed in a double-breasted dinner jacket, a little too much waisted, and a butterfly tie a good deal too large. He had a thick mat of black, wavy hair, very sleek and shiny, brushed straight back from his forehead, and large flashing eyes. He spoke with great refinement, but with a Cockney accent.

"How's Stella?" asked Sandy.

"Oh, she's all right. Likes to have a lay-down before the show, you know. Steadies the old nerves, she says."

"I wouldn't do that stunt of hers for a thousand pounds."

"I don't suppose you would. No one can do it but

her, not from that height, I mean, and only five foot of water."

"It's the most sick-making thing I've ever seen."

Cotman gave a little laugh. He took this as a compliment. Stella was his wife. Of course she did the trick and took the risk, but it was he who had thought of the flames, and it was the flames that had taken the public fancy and made the turn the huge success it was. Stella dived into a tank from the top of a ladder sixty feet high, and, as he said, there were only five feet of water in the tank. Just before she dived they poured enough petrol on to cover the surface and he set it alight; the flames soared up and she dived straight into them.

"Paco Espinel tells me it's the biggest draw the Casino has ever had," said Sandy.

"I know, he told me they'd served as many dinners in July as they generally do in August. 'And that's you,' he says to me."

"Well, I hope you're making a packet."

"Well, I can't exactly say that. You see, we've got our contract, and naturally we didn't know it was going to be a riot, but Mr. Espinel's talking of booking us for next month, and I don't mind telling you he's not going to get us on the same terms or anything like it. Why, I had a letter from an agent only this morning saying they wanted us to go to Deauville."

"Here are my people," said Sandy.

He nodded to Cotman and left him. Eva Barrett sailed in with the rest of her guests. She had gathered them together downstairs. It was a party of eight.

"I knew we should find you here, Sandy," she said. "I'm not late, am I?"

"Only half an hour."

"Ask them what cocktails they want, and then we'll dine."

While they were standing at the bar, emptying now, for nearly everyone had gone down to the terrace for dinner, Paco Espinel passed through and stopped to shake hands with Eva Barrett. Paco Espinel was a young man who had run through his money and now made his living by arranging the turns with which the Casino sought to attract visitors. It was his duty to be civil to the rich and great. Mrs. Chaloner Barrett was an American widow of vast wealth; she not only entertained expensively, but also gambled. And after all, the dinners and suppers and the two cabaret shows that accompanied them were provided only to induce people to lose their money at the tables.

"Got a good table for me, Paco?" said Eva Barrett.

"The best." His eyes, fine, dark Argentine eyes, expressed his admiration of Mrs. Barrett's opulent, ageing charms. This also was business. "You've seen Stella?"

"Of course. Three times. It's the most terrifying thing I've ever seen."

"Sandy comes every night."

"I want to be in at the death. She's bound to kill herself one of these nights, and I don't want to miss that if I can help it."

Paco laughed.

"She's been such a success, we're going to keep her on another month. All I ask is that she shouldn't kill herself till the end of August. After that she can do as she likes."

"Oh God, have I got to go on eating trout and roast chicken every night till the end of August?" cried Sandy.

"You brute, Sandy," said Eva Barrett. "Come on, let's go in to dinner. I'm starving."

Paco Espinel asked the barman if he'd seen Cotman.

The barman said he'd had a drink with Mr. Westcott.

"Oh well, if he comes in here again, tell him I want a word with him."

Mrs. Barrett paused at the top of the steps that led down to the terrace long enough for the press representative, a little haggard woman with an untidy head, to come up with her notebook. Sandy whispered the names of the guests. It was a representative Riviera party. There was an English lord and his lady, long and lean both of them, who were prepared to dine with anyone who would give them a free meal. They were certain to be as tight as drums before midnight. There was a gaunt Scotchwoman, with a face like a Peruvian mask that has been battered by the storms of ten centuries, and her English husband. Though a broker by profession, he was bluff, military and hearty. He gave you an impression of such integrity that you were almost more sorry for him than for yourself when the good thing he had put you onto as a special favour turned out to be a dud. There was an Italian countess who was neither Italian nor a countess but played a beautiful game of bridge, and there was a Russian prince who was ready to make Mrs. Barrett a princess and in the meantime sold champagne, motorcars and Old Masters on commission. A dance was in progress, and Mrs. Barrett, waiting for it to end, surveyed, with a look which her short upper lip made scornful, the serried throng on the dance floor. It was a gala night, and the dining tables were crowded together. Beyond the terrace the sea was calm and silent. The music stopped, and the headwaiter, affably smiling, came up to guide her to her table. She swept down the steps with majestic gait.

"We shall have quite a good view of the dive," she said as she sat down.

"I like to be next door to the tank," said Sandy, "so that I can see her face."

"Is she pretty?" asked the Countess.

"It's not that. It's the expression of her eyes. She's scared to death every time she does it."

"Oh, I don't believe that," said the City gentleman, Colonel Goodhart by name, though no one had ever discovered how he came by the title. "I mean, the whole bally stunt's only a trick. There's no danger really, I mean."

"You don't know what you're talking about. Diving from that height in as little water as that, she's got to turn like a flash the moment she touches the water. And if she doesn't do it right she's bound to bash her head against the bottom and break her back."

"That's just what I'm telling you, old boy," said the Colonel, "it's a trick. I mean, there's no argument."

"If there's no danger, there's nothing to it, anyway," said Eva Barrett. "It's over in a minute. Unless she's risking her life it's the biggest fraud of modern times. Don't say we've come to see this over and over again and it's only a fake."

"Pretty well everything is. You can take my word for that."

"Well, you ought to know," said Sandy.

If it occurred to the Colonel that this might be a nasty dig, he admirably concealed it. He laughed.

"I don't mind saying I know a thing or two," he admitted. "I mean, I've got my eyes peeled all right. You can't put much over on me."

The tank was on the far left of the terrace, and behind it, supported by stays, was an immensely tall ladder at the top of which was a tiny platform. After two or three dances more, when Eva Barrett's party were eating asparagus, the music stopped and the lights were lowered. A spot was turned on the tank. Cotman was visible in the brilliance. He ascended half a dozen steps so that he was on a level with the top of the tank.

"Ladies and gentlemen," he cried out in a loud clear voice, "you are now going to see the most marvellous feat of the century. Madame Stella, the greatest diver in the world, is about to dive from a height of sixty feet into a lake of flames five foot deep. This is a feat that has never been performed before, and Madame Stella is prepared to give one hundred pounds to any-one who will attempt it. Ladies and gentlemen, I have the honour to present Madame Stella."

A little figure appeared at the top of the steps that led onto the terrace, ran quickly up to the tank, and bowed to the applauding audience. She wore a man's silk dressing gown and on her head a bathing cap. Her thin face was made up as if for the stage. The Italian countess looked at her through her *face-à-main*.

"Not pretty," she said.

"Good figure," said Eva Barrett. "You'll see."

Stella slipped out of her dressing gown and gave it to Cotman. He went down the steps. She stood for a moment and looked at the crowd. They were in dark-ness and she could only see vague white faces and white shirt fronts. She was small, beautifully made, with legs long for her body and slim hips. Her bathing costume was very scanty.

"You're quite right about the figure, Eva," said the Colonel. "Bit undeveloped, of course, but I know you girls think that's quite the thing."

Stella began to climb the ladder, and the spotlight followed her. It seemed an incredible height. An at-tendant poured petrol on the surface of the water. Cotman was handed a flaming torch. He watched Stella reach the top of the ladder and settle herself on the platform.

"Ready?" he cried.

"Yes."

"Go," he shouted.

And as he shouted he seemed to plunge the burning torch into the water. The flames sprang up, leaping high, and really terrifying to look at. At the same moment Stella dived. She came down like a streak of lightning and plunged through the flames, which subsided a moment after she had reached the water. A second later she was at the surface and jumped out to a roar, a storm of applause. Cotman wrapped the dressing gown round her. She bowed and bowed. The applause went on. Music struck up. With a final wave of the hand she ran down the steps and between the tables to the door. The lights went up, and the waiters hurried along with their neglected service.

Sandy Westcott gave a sigh. He did not know whether he was disappointed or relieved.

"Top-hole," said the English peer.

"It's a bally fake," said the Colonel, with his British pertinacity. "I bet you anything you like."

"It's over so quickly," said her English ladyship. "I mean, you don't get your money's worth really."

Anyhow, it wasn't her money. That it never was. The Italian countess leaned forward. She spoke fluent English, but with a strong accent.

"Eva, my darling, who are those extraordinary people at the table near the door under the balcony?"

"Packet of fun, aren't they?" said Sandy. "I simply haven't been able to take my eyes off them."

Eva Barrett glanced at the table the Countess indicated, and the Prince, who sat with his back to it, turned round to look.

"They can't be true," cried Eva. "I must ask Angelo who they are."

Mrs. Barrett was the sort of woman who knew the headwaiters of all the principal restaurants in Europe by their first names. She told the waiter who was at that moment filling her glass to send Angelo to her.

It was certainly an odd pair. They were sitting by themselves at a small table. They were very old. The man was big and stout, with a mass of white hair, great bushy white eyebrows and an enormous white moustache. He looked like the late King Humbert of Italy, but much more like a king. He sat bolt upright. He wore full evening dress, with a white tie and a collar that has been out of fashion for hard on thirty years. His companion was a little old lady in a black satin ball dress, cut very low and tight at the waist. Round her neck were several chains of coloured beads. She wore what was obviously a wig, and a very ill-fitting one at that; it was very elaborate, all curls and sausages, and raven black. She was outrageously made up, bright blue under the eyes and on the eyelids, the eyebrows heavily black, a great patch of very pink rouge on each cheek and the lips a livid scarlet. The skin hung loosely on her face in deep wrinkles. She had large bold eyes, and they darted eagerly from table to table. She was taking everything in, and every other minute called the old man's attention to someone or other. The appearance of the couple was so fantastic in that fashionable crowd, the men in dinner jackets, the women in thin, pale-coloured frocks, that many eyes were turned on them. The staring did not seem to incommode the old lady. When she felt certain persons were looking at her she raised her eyebrows archly, smiled and rolled her eyes. She seemed on the point of acknowledging applause.

Angelo hurried up to the good customer that Eva Barrett was.

"You wished to see me, my lady?"

"Oh, Angelo, we're simply dying to know who those absolutely marvellous people are at the table next to the door."

Angelo gave a look and then assumed a deprecating air. The expression of his face, the movement of his shoulders, the turn of his spine, the gesture of his hands, probably even the twiddle of his toes, all indicated a half-humorous apology.

"You must overlook them, my lady." He knew of course that Mrs. Barrett had no right to be thus addressed, just as he knew that the Italian countess was neither Italian nor a countess and that the English lord never paid for a drink if anyone else would pay for it, but he also knew that to be thus addressed did not displease her. "They begged me to give them a table because they wanted to see Madame Stella do her dive. They were in the profession themselves once. I know they're not the sort of people one expects to see dining here, but they made such a point of it I simply hadn't the heart to refuse."

"But I think they're a perfect scream. I adore them."

"I've known them for many years. The man indeed is a compatriot of mine." The headwaiter gave a condescending little laugh. "I told them I'd give them a table on the condition that they didn't dance. I wasn't taking any risks, my lady."

"Oh, but I should have loved to see them dance."

"One has to draw the line somewhere, my lady," said Angelo gravely.

He smiled, bowed again and withdrew.

"Look," cried Sandy, "they're going."

The funny old couple were paying their bill. The

old man got up and put round his wife's neck a large white, but not too clean, feather boa. She rose. He gave her his arm, holding himself very erect, and she, small in comparison, tripped out beside him. Her black satin dress had a long train, and Eva Barrett (who was well over fifty) screamed with joy.

"Look, I remember my mother wearing a dress like that when I was in the schoolroom."

The comic pair walked, still arm in arm, through the spacious rooms of the Casino till they came to the door. The old man addressed a commissionaire.

"Be so good as to direct me to the artistes' dressing rooms. We wish to pay our respects to Madame Stella."

The commissionaire gave them a look and summed them up. They were not people with whom it was necessary to be very polite.

"You won't find her there."

"She has not gone? I thought she gave a second performance at two."

"That's true. They might be in the bar."

"It won't 'urt us just to go an' 'ave a look, Carlo," said the old lady.

"Right-o, my love," he answered with a great roll of the R.

They walked slowly up the great stairs and entered the bar. It was empty but for the deputy barman and a couple sitting in two armchairs in the corner. The old lady released her husband's arm and tripped up with outstretched hands.

" 'Ow are you, dear? I felt I just 'ad to come and congratulate you, bein' English same as you are. And in the profession meself. It's a grand turn, my dear, it deserves to be a success." She turned to Cotman. "And is this your 'usband?"

Stella got out of her armchair and a shy smile broke on her lips as she listened with some confusion to the voluble old lady.

"Yes, that's Syd."

"Pleased to meet you," he said.

"And this is mine," said the old lady, with a little dig of the elbow in the direction of the tall, white-haired man. "Mr. Penezzi. 'E's a count really, and I'm the Countess Penezzi by rights, but when we retired from the profession we dropped the title."

"Will you have a drink?" said Cotman.

"No, you 'ave one with us," said Mrs. Penezzi, sinking into an armchair. "Carlo, you order."

The barman came, and after some discussion three bottles of beer were ordered. Stella would not have anything.

"She never has anything till after the second show," explained Cotman.

Stella was slight and small, about twenty-six, with light brown hair, cut short and waved, and grey eyes. She had reddened her lips, but wore little rouge on her face. Her skin was pale. She was not very pretty, but she had a neat little face. She wore a very simple evening frock of white silk. The beer was brought, and Mr. Penezzi, evidently not very talkative, took a long swig.

"What was your line?" asked Syd Cotman politely.

Mrs. Penezzi gave him a rolling glance of her flashing, made-up eyes and turned to her husband.

"Tell 'em who I am, Carlo," she said.

"The 'Uman Cannon Ball," he announced.

Mrs. Penezzi smiled brightly and with a quick, bird-like glance looked from one to the other. They stared at her in dismay.

"Flora," she said. "The 'uman cannon ball."

She so obviously expected them to be impressed that they did not quite know what to do. Stella gave her Syd a puzzled look. He came to the rescue.

"It must have been before our time."

"Naturally it was before your time. Why, we retired from the profession definitely the year poor Queen Victoria died. It made quite a sensation when we did, too. But you've 'eard of me, of course." She saw the blank look on their faces; her tone changed a little. "But I was the biggest draw in London. At the Old Aquarium, that was. All the swells came to see me. The Prince of Wales and I don't know who all. I was the talk of the town. Isn't that true, Carlo?"

"She crowded the Aquarium for a year."

"It was the most spectacular turn they'd ever 'ad there. Why, only a few years ago I went up and introduced meself to Lady de Bathe. Lily Langtry, you know. She used to live down 'ere. She remembered me perfectly. She told me she'd seen me ten times."

"What did you do?" asked Stella.

"I was fired out of a cannon. Believe me, it was a sensation. And after London I went all over the world with it. Yes, my dear, I'm an old woman now and I won't deny it. Seventy-eight Mr. Penezzi is, and I shall never see seventy again, but I've 'ad me portrait on every 'oardin' in London. Lady de Bathe said to me: 'My dear, you was as celebrated as I was.' But you know what the public is, give 'em a good thing and they go mad over it, only they want change; 'owever good it is, they get sick of it, and then they won't go and see it any more. It'll 'appen to you, my dear, same as it 'appened to me. It comes to all of us. But Mr. Penezzi always 'ad 'is 'ead screwed on 'is shoulders the right way. Been in the business since 'e was so 'igh. Circus, you know. Ringmaster. That's 'ow I first knew 'im. I was in a troupe of acrobacks. Trapeze act, you know. 'E's a fine-lookin' man now, but you should 'ave seen 'im then, in 'is Russian boots, and ridin' breeches, and a tight-fittin' coat with frogs all down the front of it, crackin' 'is long whip as 'is 'orses galloped round the ring, the 'andsomest man I ever see in my life."

Mr. Penezzi did not make any remark, but thoughtfully twisted his immense white moustache.

"Well, as I was tellin' you, 'e was never one to throw money about and when the agents couldn't get us bookin's any more 'e said, 'Let's retire.' And 'e was quite right, after 'avin' been the biggest star in London, we couldn't go back to circus work any more; I mean, Mr. Penezzi bein' a count really, 'e 'ad 'is dignity to think of, so we come down 'ere and we bought a 'ouse and started a pension. It always 'ad been Mr. Penezzi's ambition to do something like that. Thirty-five years we been 'ere now. We 'aven't done so badly, not until the last two or three years, and the slump came, though visitors are very different from what they was when we first started, the things they want, electric light and runnin' water in their bedrooms and I don't know what all. Give them a card, Carlo. Mr. Penezzi does the cookin' 'imself, and if ever you want a real 'ome from 'ome, you'll know where to find it. I like professional people, and we'd 'ave a rare lot to talk about, you and me, dearie. Once a professional always a professional, I say."

At that moment the head barman came back from his supper. He caught sight of Syd.

"Oh, Mr. Cotman, Mr. Espinel was looking for you, wants to see you particularly."

"Oh, where is he?"

"You'll find him around somewhere."

"We'll be going," said Mrs. Penezzi, getting up.

"Come and 'ave lunch with us one day, will you? I'd like to show you my old photographs and me press cuttin's. Fancy you not 'avin' 'eard of the 'uman cannon ball. Why, I was as well known as the Tower of London."

Mrs. Penezzi was not vexed at finding that these young people had never even heard of her. She was simply amused.

They bade one another good-bye, and Stella sank back again into her chair.

"I'll just finish my beer," said Syd, "and then I'll go and see what Paco wants. Will you stay here, ducky, or would you like to go to your dressing room?"

Stella's hands were tightly clenched. She did not answer. Syd gave her a look and then quickly glanced away.

"Perfect riot, that old girl," he went on in his hearty way. "Real figure of fun. I suppose it's true what she said. It's difficult to believe, I must say. Fancy 'er drawing all London, what, forty years ago? And the funny thing is, her thinking anybody remembered. Seemed as though she simply couldn't understand us not having heard of her even."

He gave Stella another glance, from the corner of his eye so that she should not see he was looking at her, and he saw she was crying. He faltered. The tears were rolling down her pale face. She made no sound.

"What's the matter, darling?"

"Syd, I can't do it again tonight," she sobbed.

"Why on earth not?"

"I'm afraid."

He took her hand.

"I know you better than that," he said. "You're the bravest little woman in the world. Have a brandy, that'll pull you together."

"No, that'd only make it worse."

"You can't disappoint your public like that."

"That filthy public. Swine who eat too much and drink too much. A pack of chattering fools with more money than they know what to do with. I can't stick them. What do they care if I risk my life?"

"Of course it's the thrill they come for, there's no denying that," he replied uneasily. "But you know and I know, there's no risk, not if you keep your nerve."

"But I've lost my nerve, Syd. I shall kill myself."

She had raised her voice a little, and he looked round quickly at the barman. But the barman was reading the *Eclaireur de Nice* and paying no attention.

"You don't know what it looks like from up there, the top of the ladder, when I look down at the tank. I give you my word, tonight I thought I was going to faint. I tell you I can't do it again tonight, you've got to get me out of it, Syd."

"If you funk it tonight it'll be worse tomorrow."

"No, it won't. It's having to do it twice kills me. The long wait and all that. You go and see Mr. Espinel and tell him I can't give two shows a night. It's more than my nerves'll stand."

"He'll never stand for that. The whole supper trade depends on you. It's only to see you they come in then at all."

"I can't help it, I tell you I can't go on."

He was silent for a moment. The tears still streamed down her pale little face, and he saw that she was quickly losing control of herself. He had felt for some days that something was up, and he had been anxious. He had tried not to give her an opportunity to talk. He knew obscurely that it was better for her not to put into words what she felt. But he had been worried. For he loved her.

"Anyhow, Espinel wants to see me," he said.

"What about?"

"I don't know. I'll tell him you can't give the show more than once a night and see what he says. Will you wait here?"

"No, I'll go along to the dressing room."

Ten minutes later he found her there. He was in great spirits and his step was jaunty. He burst open the door.

"I've got grand news for you, honey. They're keeping us on next month at twice the money."

He sprang forward to take her in his arms and kiss her, but she pushed him away.

"Have I got to go on again tonight?"

"I'm afraid you must. I tried to make it only one show a night, but he wouldn't hear of it. He says it's quite essential you should do the supper turn. And after all, for double the money, it's worth it."

She flung herself down on the floor and this time burst into a storm of tears.

"I can't, Syd, I can't. I shall kill myself."

He sat down on the floor and raised her head and took her in his arms and petted her.

"Buck up, darling. You can't refuse a sum like that. Why, it'll keep us all the winter, and we shan't have to do a thing. After all, there are only four more days to the end of July, and then it's only August."

"No, no, no. I'm frightened. I don't want to die, Syd. I love you."

"I know you do, darling, and I love you. Why, since we married I've never looked at another woman. We've never had money like this before, and we shall never get it again. You know what these things are, we're a riot now, but we can't expect it to go on for-ever. We've got to strike while the iron's hot."

"D'you want me to die, Syd?"

"Don't talk so silly. Why, where should I be without you? You mustn't give way like this. You've got your self-respect to think of. You're famous all over the world."

"Like the human cannon ball was," she cried with a laugh of fury.

"That damned old woman," he thought.

He knew that was the last straw. Bad luck, Stella taking it like that.

"That was an eye-opener to me," she went on. "What do they come and see me over and over again for? On the chance they'll see me kill myself. And a week after I'm dead they'll have forgotten even my name. That's what the public is. When I looked at that painted old hag I saw it all. Oh, Syd, I'm so miserable." She threw her arms round his neck and pressed her face to his. "Syd, it's no good, I can't do it again."

"Tonight, d'you mean? If you really feel like that about it, I'll tell Espinel you've had a fainting fit. I daresay it'll be all right just for once."

"I don't mean tonight, I mean never."

She felt him stiffen a little.

"Syd dear, don't think I'm being silly. It's not just today, it's been growing on me. I can't sleep at night thinking of it, and when I do drop off I see myself standing at the top of the ladder and looking down. Tonight I could hardly get up it, I was trembling so, and when you lit the flames and said go, something seemed to be holding me back. I didn't even know I'd jumped. My mind was a blank till I found myself on the platform and heard them clapping. Syd, if you loved me you wouldn't want me to go through such torture."

He sighed. His own eyes were wet with tears. For he loved her devotedly.

"You know what it means," he said. "The old life. Marathons and all."

"Anything's better than this."

The old life. They both remembered it. Syd had been a dancing gigolo since he was eighteen. He was very good-looking in his dark Spanish way and full of life. Old women and middle-aged women were glad to pay to dance with him, and he was never out of work. He had drifted from England to the Continent, and there he had stayed, going from hotel to hotel, to the Riviera in the winter, to watering places in France in the summer. It wasn't a bad life they led. There were generally two or three of them together, the men, and they shared a room in cheap lodgings. They didn't have to get up till late, and they only dressed in time to go to the hotel at twelve to dance with stout women who wanted to get their weight down. Then they were free till five, when they went to the hotel again and sat at a table, the three of them together, keeping a sharp eye open for anyone who looked a likely client. They had their regular customers. At night they went to the restaurant, and the house provided them with quite a decent meal.

Between the courses they danced. It was good money. They generally got fifty or a hundred francs from anyone they danced with. Sometimes a rich woman, after dancing a good deal with one of them for two or three nights, would give him as much as a thousand francs. Sometimes a middle-aged woman would ask one to spend a night with her, and he would get two hundred and fifty francs for that. There was always the chance of a silly old fool losing her head, and then there were platinum and sapphire rings, cigarette cases, clothes and a wrist watch to be got. One of Syd's friends had married one of them who was old enough to be his mother, but she gave him a car and money to gamble with, and they lived in a beautiful villa at Biarritz. Those were the good days when everybody had money to burn. The slump came and hit the gigolos hard. The hotels were empty, and the clients didn't seem to want to pay for the pleasure of dancing with a nice-looking young fellow. Often and often Syd passed a whole day without earning the price of a drink, and more than once a fat old girl who weighed a ton had had the nerve to give him ten francs. His expenses didn't go down, for he had to be smartly dressed or the manager of the hotel made remarks, washing cost a packet, and you'd be surprised the amount of linen he needed; then shoes, those floors were terribly hard on shoes, and they had to look new. He had his room to pay for and his lunch.

It was then he met Stella. It was at Evian, and the season was disastrous. She was a swimming instructress. She was Australian and a beautiful diver. She gave exhibitions every morning and afternoon. At night she was engaged to dance at the hotel. They dined together at a little table in the restaurant apart from the guests, and when the band began to play they danced together to induce the customers to come onto the floor. But often no one followed them and they danced by themselves. Neither of them got anything much in the way of paying partners. They fell in love with one another, and at the end of the season got married.

They had never regretted it. They had gone through hard times. Even though for business reasons (elderly ladies didn't so much like the idea of dancing with a married man when his wife was there) they concealed

116

their marriage, it was not so easy to get a hotel job for the pair of them, and Syd was far from being able to earn enough to keep Stella, even in the most modest pension, without working. The gigolo business had gone to pot. They went to Paris and learnt a dancing act, but the competition was fearful and cabaret engagements were very hard to get. Stella was a good ballroom dancer, but the rage was for acrobatics, and however much they practised, she never managed to do anything startling. The public was sick of the apache turn. They were out of a job for weeks at a time. Syd's wrist watch, his gold cigarette case, his platinum ring, all went up the spout. At last they found themselves in Nice reduced to such straits that Syd had to pawn his evening clothes. It was a catastrophe. They were forced to enter for the Marathon that an enterprising manager was starting. Twenty-four hours a day they danced, resting every hour for fifteen minutes. It was frightful. Their legs ached, their feet were numb. For long periods they were unconscious of what they were doing. They just kept time to the music, exerting themselves as little as possible. They made a little money, people gave them sums of a hundred francs, or two hundred, to encourage them, and sometimes to attract attention they roused themselves to give an exhibition dance. If the public was in a good humour, this might bring in a decent sum. They grew terribly tired. On the eleventh day Stella fainted and had to give up. Syd went on by himself, moving, moving without pause, grotesquely, without a partner. That was the worst time they had ever had. It was the final degradation. It had left with them a recollection of horror and misery.

But it was then that Syd had his inspiration. It had come to him while he was slowly going round the hall by himself. Stella always said she could dive in a saucer. It was just a trick.

"Funny how ideas come," he said afterwards. "Like a flash of lightning."

He suddenly remembered having seen a boy set fire to some petrol that had been spilt on the pavement, and the sudden blaze-up. For of course it was the flames on the water and the spectacular dive into them that had caught the public fancy. He stopped dancing there and then; he was too excited to go on. He talked it over with Stella, and she was enthusiastic. He wrote to an agent who was a friend of his—everyone liked Syd, he was a nice little man—and the agent put up the money for the apparatus. He got them an engagement at the circus in Paris, and the turn was a success. They were made. Engagements followed here and there. Syd bought himself an entire outfit of new clothes, and the climax came when they got a booking for the summer casino on the coast. It was no exaggeration of Syd's when he said that Stella was a riot.

"All our troubles are over, old girl," he said fondly. "We can put a bit by now for a rainy day, and when the public's sick of this I'll just think of something else."

And now, without warning, at the top of their boom, Stella wanted to chuck it. He didn't know what to say to her. It broke his heart to see her so unhappy. He loved her more now even than when he had married her. He loved her because of all they'd gone through together—after all, for five days once they'd had nothing to eat but a hunk of bread each and a glass of milk—and he loved her because she'd taken him out of all that; he had good clothes to wear again and his three meals a day. He couldn't look at her; the anguish in her dear grey eyes was more than he could bear.

118

Timidly she stretched out her hand and touched his. He gave a deep sigh.

"You know what it means, honey. Our connection in the hotels has gone west, and the business is finished anyway. What there is'll go to people younger than us. You know what these old women are as well as I do, it's a boy they want, and besides, I'm not tall enough really. It didn't matter so much when I was a kid. It's no good saying I don't look my age, because I do."

"Perhaps we can get into pictures."

He shrugged his shoulders. They'd tried that before when they were down and out.

"I wouldn't mind what I did. I'd serve in a shop."

"D'you think jobs can be had for the asking?"

She began to cry again.

"Don't, honey. It breaks my heart."

"We've got a bit put by."

"I know we have. Enough to last us six months. And then it'll mean starvation. First popping the bits and pieces, and then the clothes'll have to go, same as they did before. And then dancing in low-down joints for our supper and fifty francs a night. Out of a job for weeks together. And Marathons whenever we hear of one. And how long will the public stand for them?"

"I know you think I'm unreasonable, Syd."

He turned and looked at her now. There were tears in her eyes. He smiled, and the smile he gave her was charming and tender.

"No, I don't, ducky. I want to make you happy. After all, you're all I've got. I love you."

He took her in his arms and held her. He could feel the beating of her heart. If Stella felt like that about it, well, he must just make the best of it. After all, supposing she were killed? No, no, let her chuck it and be damned to the money. She made a little movement.

"What is it, honey?"

She released herself and stood up. She went over to the dressing table.

"I expect it's about time for me to be getting ready," she said.

He started to his feet.

"You're not going to do a show tonight?"

"Tonight, and every night till I kill myself. What else is there? I know you're right, Syd. I can't go back to all that other, stinking rooms in fifth-rate hotels and not enough to eat. Oh, that Marathon. Why did you bring that up? Being tired and dirty for days at a time and then having to give up because flesh and blood just couldn't stand it. Perhaps I can go on another month and then there'll be enough to give you a chance of looking round."

"No, darling, I can't stand for that. Chuck it. We'll manage somehow. We starved before; we can starve again."

She slipped out of her clothes, and for a moment stood naked but for her stockings, looking at herself in the glass. She gave her reflection a hard smile.

"I mustn't disappoint my public," she sniggered.

GIGOLO AND GIGOLETTE

List of Cast

Character	*Artiste*
STELLA COTMAN	GLYNIS JOHNS
SYD COTMAN	TERENCE MORGAN
FLORA PENEZZI	MARY MERRALL
CARLO PENEZZI	MARTIN MILLER
PACO ESPINEL	CHARLES GOLDNER
SANDY WESTCOTT	DAVID HUTCHESON
EVA BARRETT	HEATHER THATCHER
RUSSIAN PRINCE	GUIDO LORRAINE
ITALIAN COUNTESS	DAPHNE BARKER
ANGELO	FERDY MAYNE
ATTENDANT	PAUL ARMSTRONG
ATTENDANT	JEAN BUIRON
ATTENDANT	NICHOLAS BRUCE
BAND LEADER	GUY DU MONCEAU
FIRST BARMAN	GASTON RICHER
SECOND BARMAN	MICHAEL ALLEN
FAT WOMAN	JOAN INGRAM
FRENCH AGENT	ARTHUR GOMEZ
CROUPIER	CLAUDE FREDERIC
CROUPIER	JACQUES CEY
CROUPIER	OSCAR NATION
CAISSIER	JOHN SERRETT
WHITE-BEARDED MAN	HENRI DE BRAY
AGENT'S RECEPTIONIST	MARGARET JOHNS

1. MR. MAUGHAM: "Gigolo and Gigolette" is a story about two people in the show business. In it you are going to see something of their lives from the inside. For my part I wish there were laws to prevent them from risking life and limb night after night to give the public a morbid thrill, but there aren't, and so to earn a hazardous living they will continue to break their backs and break their necks for your amusement.

DISSOLVE

2. *Insert. The first page of the story: GIGOLO AND GIGOLETTE. The narrator begins to read.*
NARRATOR: The food in the restaurant at the Ritz Hotel in Monte Carlo was expensive but good.

DISSOLVE

3. *Exterior Monte Carlo. Night. (Location.) General long shot of Monte Carlo at night.*

DISSOLVE

4. *Exterior Ritz Hotel terrace. Night. A group of people arrive and are met by the headwaiter. The camera pans with them as they are escorted through the tables to seats in front of the orchestra. The tables and the dance floor are crowded. Beyond the terrace can be seen the lights of Monte Carlo and a calm sea. The dance music is faintly heard behind the narrator's voice.*
NARRATOR: . . . The orchestra was highly paid; and there were two cabaret shows, besides other, more sensational entertainment. These were the means by which the management sought to attract visitors, and get them to win or lose money at the gambling tables.

DISSOLVE

5. *Interior Ritz Hotel bar and foyer. Night. Shooting towards the entrance of the bar, from inside the bar. This is just off the main corridor and stairs leading from the street to the restaurant. In the background, through the large windows, other distant lights are visible. Coming through the door is Syd Cotman. He is a nice-looking fel-*

*low, of thirty perhaps, short, but with so good a figure that
he does not look it. He is very smartly dressed in a double-
breasted dinner jacket, a little too much waisted, and a
butterfly tie a good deal too large. He speaks with great
refinement, but with a Cockney accent.*

NARRATOR: It was a gala night and the bar was crowded.

*He goes over and joins Sandy Westcott at the bar. Sandy
Westcott has had a couple of cocktails and is beginning to
feel hungry. As he turns to the barman to order another
cocktail, he catches sight of Syd.*

SANDY: Hullo, Cotman. Have a drink?

SYD: I don't mind if I do, sir. Scotch, thanks.

SANDY (*to barman*): Scotch and a dry martini. (*To Syd*)
How's your wife?

SYD: Oh, Stella's all right. Likes to have a lay-down
before the show, you know. Steadies the old nerves, she
says.

SANDY: I wouldn't do that stunt of hers for ten thousand
pounds.

SYD: I don't suppose you would. No one can do it but
her, not from that height, I mean, and only five foot of
water.

SANDY (*handing Syd a drink*): Terrifying. Paco Espinel
says it's the biggest draw the Ritz ever had.

SYD: Well, I'm glad he admits it. I do know they've
served as many dinners in July as they usually do in
August. (*Raises glass*) Salut!

SANDY: Cheers. I hope you're making a packet.

SYD: Well, I can't exactly say that. You see, we've got
our contract and naturally we didn't know it was going to
be a riot. Still, Paco Espinel is talking of booking us for
next month, and I don't mind telling you he's not going
to get us on the same terms or anything like. Why, I had
a letter from an agent only this morning saying they
wanted us to go to Deauville, and the money they're
offering . . .

But Sandy has caught sight of someone off.

SANDY (*going*): Excuse me . . . here are my people.

Sandy goes without waiting to hear more.

SYD: Sure.

*He drinks his whisky and goes out in the opposite
direction.*

6. *Interior Ritz Hotel bar. Night. Eva Barrett has entered with three of her guests and is coming towards camera. She is an American widow of vast wealth. Sandy walks into shot and joins her.*

EVA BARRETT: I knew we should find you here, Sandy. I'm not too late, am I?

SANDY: Only half an hour.

But Mrs. Barrett does not hear. Her attention has been taken by a young man in tails who is bowing to her.

EVA BARRETT: Hullo, Paco. Got a good table for me?

Paco Espinel is a young man who has run through his money and now makes a good living arranging the entertainments at the Ritz. His eyes, fine, dark Argentine eyes, express his admiration of Mrs. Barrett's opulent, ageing charms. This also is part of his job. They shake hands.

PACO: The best, of course. You've seen Stella?

EVA BARRETT: Three times. It's the most frightening thing I've ever seen.

In Mrs. Barrett's party there is a Russian prince. He would have no objection to making her a princess.

PRINCE: Only three? Sandy comes every night.

SANDY: I want to be in at the death. She's bound to kill herself one of these nights, and I don't want to miss that if I can help it.

PACO (*laughing*): She's been such a success, we're going to keep her on another month. All I ask is that she shouldn't kill herself till the end of August. After that she can do as she likes.

SANDY: Oh, my goodness, have I got to go on eating trout and roast chicken every night till the end of August?

EVA BARRETT: You brute, Sandy. Come on, let's go into dinner, I'm starving.

As they start to move off . . .

7. *Interior Ritz Hotel bar. Night. Shooting from behind the bar. Eva Barrett and her party move away from the bar and Paco makes his way to the bar, towards camera. The others move off towards the terrace. Without his smile, Paco looks quite shrewd. The barman is immediately attentive.*

PACO: Have you seen Mr. Cotman?

BARMAN: He was here a few moments ago, sir. He had a drink with Mr. Westcott.

PACO: Oh well, if he comes in here again, tell him I want a word with him in the office this evening.

BARMAN: Yes, sir.

At that moment the music from the terrace orchestra ends and there is a resounding roll of drums. One or two of those in the bar quickly put down their drinks and make for the terrace entrance. Paco turns in that direction.

8. *Exterior Ritz Hotel terrace. Night. The floor is clearing quickly as the drum roll continues, then it ceases with a cymbal crash. At that instant four arc lights are trained on a cylindrical tank about twelve feet across, standing just over five feet above the floor level. The four arcs hold there for a moment, then two of them pick up the ladder —as they start to move up the ladder . . .*

9. *Exterior Ritz Hotel terrace. Night. Eva Barrett's party is just sitting down at a table near the tank. In the party, besides Sandy and the prince, are an English lord and an Italian countess.*

EVA BARRETT (*sitting*): We shall have quite a good view of the dive.

SANDY: I like to be right next to the tank.

PRINCE: But why, please?

SANDY: So that I can see her face.

COUNTESS: Is she pretty?

SANDY: It's not that. It's the expression of her eyes, in my opinion. She's scared to death every time she does it.

PRINCE: Oh, I don't believe that. It is undoubtedly a phony.

SANDY: You don't know what you're talking about. (*Demonstrating with his hand*) Diving from that height in as little water as that, she's got to turn like a flash the moment she touches the water. And if she doesn't do it right she's bound to bash her head against the bottom and break her back.

PRINCE: Oh, there's no danger.

EVA BARRETT: If there's no danger, there's nothing to it, anyway. It's over in a minute. Unless she's risking her life, it's the biggest swindle I've ever heard of.

PRINCE: Pretty well everything is a swindle. You can take my word for that.

SANDY: Well, you should know, Prince.

Before the prince can decide quite how to take this, there is another roll of drums and another battery of arcs illuminates a space on the floor.

10. *Exterior Ritz Hotel terrace. Night. Long shot. Into this illuminated space comes Syd. He is in a white dinner jacket now. For a moment or two he stands quite still. The sounds of the place die down. Syd is a showman.*

SYD: Ladies and gentlemen. You are now going to see the most marvellous feat of the century. Madame Stella, the greatest diver in the world, is about to dive from a height of eighty feet into a lake of flames five foot deep. This is a feat that has never been performed before, and Madame Stella is prepared to give one thousand pounds to anyone who will attempt it. Ladies and gentlemen, I have the honour to present Madame Stella!

As Syd steps back, the arcs swing to the steps as Stella makes her entrance. As she starts to come down the steps . . .

11. *Exterior Ritz Hotel terrace. Night. Closer shot of Stella as she comes down the steps to join Syd. She bows to the applauding audience. She smiles faintly. She is a favourite.*

12. *Exterior Ritz Hotel terrace. Night. Shooting on to Eva Barrett's table. The Countess looks at her through a very chic monocular quizzing glass.*

COUNTESS: Not pretty.

EVA BARRETT: Good figure. You'll see.

13. *Exterior Ritz Hotel terrace. Night. Another angle. As she finishes her bow, Stella turns and walks over to the tank. The lights follow her. She stops. Syd is beside her. She slips out of her dressing gown. He takes it from her.*

14. *Exterior Ritz Hotel terrace. Night. Shooting on to Eva Barrett's table.*

PRINCE: You're quite right about the figure, Eva. A little underdeveloped, of course.

15. *Exterior Ritz Hotel terrace. Night. Long shot of Stella as she begins to climb the ladder, with Syd in foreground. He steps forward again into the lights.*

SYD: Ladies and gentlemen, this amazing feat is made possible only by Madame Stella's supreme judgment and skill. It requires absolute concentration. The slightest distraction might prove fatal.

15a. *Extreme long shot of Stella climbing the ladder as Syd continues his announcement.*

SYD: I must therefore ask you when I give the word to remain absolutely still and silent. Thank you. *Mesdames et messieurs . . .*

16. *Exterior Ritz Hotel terrace. Night. Closer shot of Stella as she climbs steadily up the glittering ladder, a spot following her. It seems an incredible height. Syd's French announcement continuing off.*

SYD (*off*): *. . . cet étonnant tour de force ne peut réussir que grâce à la suprême habileté et au prodigieux jugement de Madame Stella. Il exige une concentration absolue. La moindre distraction pourrait être fatale. Je vais donc vous prier, lorsque j'en donnerai le signal, de vous tenir absolument immobiles et d'observer le plus profond silence.*

Halfway through his French announcement . . . Audience reaction to Stella and Syd.

17. *Exterior Ritz Hotel terrace. Night. Reverse shot of Syd. At the end of his announcement he looks up.*

18. *Exterior Ritz Hotel terrace. Night. Medium shot of Stella. She has reached the diving board at the top of the ladder.*

19. *Exterior Ritz Hotel terrace. Night. Medium shot of Syd. He nods to an attendant who pours petrol on the surface of the water in the tank. A long drum roll begins.*

20. *Exterior Ritz Hotel terrace. Night. Stella walks to the edge of the diving board.*

21. *Exterior Ritz Hotel terrace. Night. Medium long shot. Syd takes a flashing torch handed to him by an attendant and walks to the middle of the floor. He holds the torch*

aloft. The drum roll stops abruptly. The torch still held aloft, Syd faces the audience.

SYD: Ladies and gentlemen. Absolute silence, please.

22. *Exterior Ritz Hotel terrace. Night. Close reverse shot. Syd turns from the audience and faces the tank, the torch still held aloft. There is dead silence in which faint sounds of traffic in the streets outside can be heard. A champagne cork pops and somebody laughs. Syd glances at the offender. There is silence.*

SYD: Are you ready, Madame Stella?
STELLA (*off*): Yes.
Syd starts to walk towards the tank.

23. *Exterior Ritz Hotel terrace. Night. Syd walks to the tank, stops and looks up. Extreme long shot.*

SYD: Go!
As he shouts the word, he dashes the torch into the tank. With a whoosh the petrol takes light, the flames leaping up. At the same time the drums roll. All eyes go to Stella.

Her hands go up. She dives. She plunges through the flames, which subside a second after she reaches the water. A moment later she is at the surface. There is a storm of applause as she appears and is helped out by Syd. Audience reaction shots and applause.

24. *Exterior Ritz Hotel terrace. Night. Medium shot of Syd taking the dressing gown from the attendant and wrapping it round her. She bows and bows.*

25. *Exterior Ritz Hotel terrace. Night. Audience applauding. Shot of Flora, Carlo "applauding."*

26. *Exterior Ritz Hotel terrace. Night. Shooting on to Eva Barrett's table. Sandy Westcott sighs.*

COUNTESS: It's over so quickly. One doesn't get one's money's worth really.

EVA BARRETT: Well, thank goodness we can order dinner now.

27. *Interior Ritz Hotel passage and dressing room. Night. Tracking shot. Swing doors at one end of the passage separate the plushy grandeur of the Ritz's public rooms from*

the bare severity of the artistes' dressing rooms. Stella comes through the swing doors, followed by Syd. The camera tracks back with them as they walk down the passage.

SYD: You're imagining it.

STELLA: I tell you the board was slack again. Somebody slackened it.

SYD: Now, darling, why . . .

STELLA: I know because I touched the side of the tank, and it wasn't because I turned late. The board was slack.

SYD: Darling . . .

He breaks off as two girls belonging to the cabaret come out of their dressing room and pass them. Stella turns into her own dressing room.

28. *Interior Stella's dressing room. Night. Stella comes into the dressing room and Syd follows her in quickly, shutting the door behind him. Stella sits down on the long stool in front of her dressing table. She takes off her fall and towels her head vigorously.*

SYD: Now, Stella, look here. Nobody touched the board. It was just as it always is. I checked up to see. I always check up. You know that.

He puts his hands on her shoulders. She puts her towel down. A pause. She puts her cheek against one of his hands. Then, suddenly, she buries her face in her hands.

STELLA: I know you do, darling, but I had such a scare.

He sinks down beside her on the stool. He speaks very gently.

SYD: Now, now. *There.* You're just tired, that's all. It's those sleeping pills. I don't think you got a proper rest with those things.

She pulls herself together a little.

STELLA: I'm all right.

He smiles.

SYD: Well, I should hope so. We can't have you getting sick now, you know. And it's only for a little while longer, darling.

STELLA: I'll be all right.

SYD: I know what you need. A drink. Slip on your frock and we'll have a glass of champagne in the bar.

She looks up at him.

STELLA: Yes, I expect that's what I need. You do love me, Syd? Even if I'm silly?

SYD: Of course I love you. Now come on and get out of those wet things.

DISSOLVE

29. *Exterior Ritz Hotel terrace. Night. Medium shot. Among the diners near Eva Barrett's table is an odd pair. They are sitting by themselves at a small table. They are very old. The man has an imposing mass of white hair, and bushy white eyebrows. He wears full evening dress of an old-fashioned kind. His companion is a little old lady in a black satin ball dress cut very low and tight at the waist. Round her neck are several chains of coloured beads. She is outrageously made-up, but the skin hangs loosely on her face. They are Carlo and Flora Penezzi. They applaud vigorously and for a moment longer than the rest. Then Carlo takes a wallet from his pocket.*

CARLO: Shall we go now, my love?

His accent is Italian.

FLORA: Yes, do let's.

Her accent is Cockney.

The bill is there on a plate. Carlo puts some money on it. As they rise, waiters come forward to remove their chairs. Carlo nods graciously to the waiters and holds Flora's shawl for her. She arranges it on her shoulders and they move towards the exit, the camera panning with them. As they pass Eva Barrett's table they move on and out of picture, the camera holding on Eva Barrett's table.

COUNTESS: But who are they?

EVA BARRETT: They can't be true! I must ask Angelo.

She raises her hand. Angelo, the headwaiter, hurries up.

ANGELO: My lady?

Eva Barrett gestures humourously in the direction of the Penezzis.

EVA BARRETT: We can't wait to know.

Angelo smiles deprecatingly. He speaks softly and quickly.

ANGELO: They begged me to give them a table because they wanted to see Madame Stella do her dive. They were in the profession themselves once.

EVA BARRETT: But I think they're heaven.

30. *Exterior Ritz Hotel terrace. Night. Long shot from the eyeline of the people at Eva Barrett's table. As the Penezzis reach the foot of the steps up to the exit, Carlo offers Flora his arm.*

31. *Exterior Ritz Hotel terrace. Night. Reverse shot from the top of the steps from the terrace. Carlo and Flora come up to the top of the steps. Flora has a long train. Everyone who sees them stares. Carlo addresses a uniformed attendant.*

CARLO: Be so good as to direct us to the artistes' dressing rooms. We wish to pay our respects to Madame Stella.

The attendant decides that they are not people with whom it is necessary to be very polite.

ATTENDANT: Madame Stella? You won't find her there.

CARLO: She has not gone? I thought she gave a second performance at two.

ATTENDANT: That's true. They might be in the bar.

FLORA: It won't hurt us to go and have a look, Carlo.

CARLO: Righto, my love.

32. *Interior Ritz Hotel bar. Night. Stella and Syd are sitting in two armchairs in a corner of the bar. They are drinking glasses of champagne. Stella puts hers down. Syd, very watchful of her, lowers his own glass immediately.*

SYD: Better?

She flashes him a friendly smile.

SYD: That's right. (*He looks across at a second barman.*) Hey, Phillips! *Encore deux coupes.*

SECOND BARMAN: O.K.

STELLA: No, no more for me.

SYD: Well, see how you feel. You know I can't bear to see you upset.

She looks up at him with pathetic eagerness.

STELLA: Oh, Syd . . .

She breaks off and her expression changes as she sees someone beyond and above him. Flora is looking down at her.

FLORA: Excuse me, dear. I felt I just had to come and congratulate you, being English same as you are. And in the profession myself. It's a grand act, my dear, and it deserves to be a success. Is this your husband?

Stella and Syd rise awkwardly.

STELLA: Yes, this is Syd.

SYD: Pleased to meet you.

FLORA: And this is mine. (*She indicates Carlo, who bows.*) Mr. Penezzi. He's a count really, and I'm the Countess Penezzi by rights, but when we retired from the profession we dropped the title.

SYD: Will you have a drink?

FLORA (*sitting*): No, you have one with us. Carlo, you order.

Carlo snaps his fingers at the second barman as Stella and Syd resume their seats.

CARLO: Champagne.

SYD (*politely to Flora*): What was your line?

FLORA: Tell them who I am, Carlo.

CARLO (*announcing*): The 'Uman Cannon Ball!

Flora watches their faces. Syd and Stella stare at her perplexed.

FLORA: Yes . . . Flora, the Human Cannon Ball.

It means nothing. Syd makes an effort.

SYD: It must have been before our time.

FLORA: Oh, naturally. Why, we retired from the profession the same year as Melba. It made quite a sensation when we did, too. But you've heard of me, of course.

She sees the blank look on their faces. Her tone changes a little.

FLORA: I was the biggest draw in London. At the old Aquarium, that was. All the swells came to see me. The King Teddy and I don't know who all. I was the talk of the town. Isn't that true, Carlo?

The second barman brings the two glasses of champagne.

CARLO: She crowded the Aquarium for a year.

FLORA: It was the most spectacular act they'd ever had.

STELLA: But what did you do?

FLORA: I was fired out of a cannon. Believe me, it was a real sensation. But you know what the public is, they only want a change. However good it is, they get sick of it and then they won't go and see it no more. It'll happen to you, my dear, same as it happened to me. It comes to all of us. But Mr. Penezzi always had his head screwed on right.

She pats Carlo's knee, and he twirls his moustache.

CARLO: What's the good of going on risking your neck

when they don't care any more? So we came down here
and bought a café.

FLORA (*she picks up her glass*): Here's to you both.

SYD: Cheers . . . (*They drink.*) We're going into the
car hire business when we've got a bit of capital together.

CARLO: Ah . . . that is good.

STELLA: What you did . . . was it very risky?

Syd glances at her quickly.

FLORA: Not if you kept your head it wasn't. And I never
lost mine. (*She grins roguishly.*) Except over Mr. Penezzi.
It was a proper love match, I can tell you, and in a thing
like that, as long as you love each other everything's safe.
Isn't that right, Carlo?

CARLO: That's right, my love.

Stella is listening intently.

FLORA: It's funny, isn't it? With ordinary people, they
have a bust-up or get fussed over something, and all that
happens is they lose their gloves or scratch themselves with
a safety pin. But with us it's different. Do you remember
the Patanellis?

*The first barman has entered. He pauses on his way to
the bar.*

FIRST BARMAN: Oh, Mr. Cotman, Mr. Espinel was looking for you. Wants to see you particularly.

SYD: Oh, where is he?

FIRST BARMAN: In his office, I think.

Flora and Carlo rise.

FLORA: We'll be going.

*Stella and Syd rise. Carlo puts money on the table for
the drinks.*

FLORA: We just wanted to congratulate you.

STELLA: Who were the Patanellis?

FLORA: Oh, they were a high-wire act. You must have
heard of them. Very sad it was. You know they never used
a net and Mrs. Patanelli fell. She was right out on the wire
and suddenly she stopped and couldn't move. Lost her
nerve. It was awful. She just stayed there for about a full
minute quite still. And then the people in the audience
began screaming and the poor little thing fell. They
couldn't understand it, but we guessed. We dressed in the
next tent and that day we'd heard she and Mr. Patanelli
have a row. He said he was sick of her. She said she didn't

133

care but she fell just the same. Tragic, wasn't it? But you don't have to worry. I could tell the moment I saw you here together just now. They're all right, I said.

Syd (*heartily*): Yes, that's right.

Flora: Come on, Carlo. (*To Syd*) Come and have a drink with us one day, will you, dear? I'd like to show you my photographs and press cuttings.

Syd: Yes, we'd like to. Good-bye.

Flora: ⎫
Carlo: ⎭ Good-bye.

Stella: Good-bye.

Stella sinks back into her chair. Syd sits beside her.

Syd: I'll just finish my drink and then I'll go and see what Paco wants. Will you stay here, dear, or would you like to go to the dressing room?

Stella's hands are tightly clenched. She does not answer. Syd glances at her quickly and then looks away.

Syd: What about the old girl! Isn't she a riot! Fancy her being a draw. And him too! (*He twirls an imaginary moustache in a parody of Carlo.*) "That's right, my love."

He glances at her again to see if he is making her smile and then falters. There are tears rolling down her cheeks.

Syd: What's the matter, darling?

Stella (*with a sob*): Syd, I can't do it again tonight.

Syd: Why on earth not?

Stella: I'm afraid.

He takes her hand.

Syd: I know you better than that. You're the bravest thing in the world. Have a brandy. That'll pull you together.

He goes to signal to the barman.

Stella: No, that'd only make it worse.

Syd: But you can't disappoint your public like that.

Stella: That public! A pack of chattering fools with more money than they know what to do with. What do they care?

Syd (*uneasily*): Well, of course, it is the thrill they come for. But you know, and I know, there's no risk, not if you keep your nerve.

Stella (*desperately*): But I've lost my nerve, Syd.

She has raised her voice a little and Syd looks round quickly. But the barman is reading the Eclaireur de Nice

*and is paying no attention. A man going to the bar nods at
Syd, who smiles back.*

SYD: Gently, darling.

STELLA: You don't know what it looks like from up
there, the top of the ladder, when I look down at the tank.
I tell you I can't do it again tonight. You've got to get me
out of it, Syd.

SYD: If you funk tonight, it'll be worse tomorrow.

STELLA: No, it won't. It's just having to do it twice. Syd,
you've got to tell Mr. Espinel I can't give two shows a
night.

SYD: But he'll never agree. The whole supper trade depends on us. It's only to see you they come at all.

STELLA: I can't help it. I tell you I can't go on.

*He sees that she is losing control of herself, and is afraid
of a scene in the bar.*

SYD: Well, anyway, Espinel wants to see me.

STELLA (*suspiciously*): What about?

SYD: I don't know. Anyway, I'll tell him you've had a
fainting fit or something and see what he says. Will you
wait here?

STELLA: I'm not going on again, Syd.

SYD: All right, I'll tell him. Where will you be? The
dressing room?

She shakes her head slowly. She doesn't quite trust him.

STELLA: No. I'm going to the hotel.

*A pause. He recognizes her distrust. A note of hostility
comes into his voice.*

SYD (*getting up*): I see.

She looks up quickly, pleading.

STELLA: Syd.

SYD: I suppose you'd rather go back to the old life. (*He
sees her expression and, relenting, pats her hand.*) It's all
right. I'll see you later.

*He goes out and Stella watches him go. The narrator's
voice is heard. Music begins.*

NARRATOR: The old life. They both remembered it.

33. *Interior Ritz Hotel foyer. Night. Syd walks down the
corridor, drawing aside to let a group of customers pass, as
the narrator continues.*

NARRATOR: Syd had been a gigolo, going from hotel to

hotel, to the Riviera in the winter, to watering places farther north in the summer. He had met Stella at Evian.

DISSOLVE

34. *Exterior Swimming pool. Day. A fat woman dives clumsily into the pool. Syd and Stella, watching her, turn to each other and smile.*

NARRATOR: She was a swimming instructress . . .

DISSOLVE

35. *Interior Evian Hotel. Night. Among the couples dancing are Syd with the fat woman and Stella with a white-bearded man.*

NARRATOR: . . . and at night she too was engaged to dance at the hotel.

Behind their partners' backs, Stella and Syd smile at one another. The smiles go as both partners tread on their feet.

NARRATOR: Neither of them got much in the way of paying partners. Instead . . .

DISSOLVE

36. *Interior Evian Hotel. Night. Stella (different dress) and Syd are dancing with one another.*

NARRATOR: . . . they fell in love with one another, and at the end of the season they got married.

DISSOLVE

37. *Interior French agent's office. Day. Stella and Syd stand in a queue in front of the receptionist's desk. They are poorly dressed. The girl in front of them is given an audition voucher by the receptionist and turns away smiling. Stella and Syd move forward.*

NARRATOR: They went through hard times together . . . for months on end they had no regular work at all . . .

The receptionist shakes her head apologetically and Stella and Syd turn away miserably.

NARRATOR: . . . and there were moments when they were . . .

DISSOLVE

38. *Interior French municipal pawnbroker's counter. Day. Syd pushes his tail suit across the counter. The pawnbroker*

*takes it and holds up the jacket to look at it. Stella and Syd
watch the pawnbroker anxiously.*

NARRATOR: . . . almost starving. And then Syd had the
idea of the dive.

DISSOLVE

39. *Interior French restaurant. Day. Syd is excitedly explaining the idea of the dive with a tower of wineglasses
and an ash tray. His audience consists of Stella and a sharp-
looking agent. The agent leans forward interestedly.*

NARRATOR: He sold the idea to a manager. When it
turned out to be a success, it seemed as if all their troubles
were over at last, and that they could be secure.

*Stella anxiously watches the agent's face. Music ends as
we . . .*

DISSOLVE

40. *Exterior Ritz Hotel terrace. Night. Syd comes down
steps to terrace and walks towards service entrance. As he
crosses the terrace, we hold on girl singer and cabaret. Syd
passes out of shot.*

40a. *Interior hotel bedroom. Night. It is in a back-street
hotel in Monte Carlo. Flowered wallpaper. Two greasy
armchairs, several suitcases. Little room to move about.*

*The lights are out. Stella, in a dressing gown, sits by the
open window through which light comes from windows
across the street. There is a radio playing somewhere.
There is the sound of quick footsteps from the passage
outside. Stella looks up. Syd comes in. Light from the passage shines into the room. For a moment he does not see
her in the darkness. Then he does.*

SYD: Here, what are you doing sitting in the dark?

*He switches on one of the two lights on the wall over
the beds and flings off his jacket.*

STELLA: It seemed cooler. What did he say?

*There is a certain artificiality about Syd's cheeriness. He
has something to conceal.*

SYD: Well, he wasn't too pleased, I can tell you. (*He
goes up to her and kisses her.*) I didn't think he would be,
of course.

STELLA: But you explained to him.

137

Syd (*warily*): Well, I worked the fainting-fit gag. (*Hurrying on*) But let's not bother about that. I've got great news. They're keeping us on next month at twice the money. What do you think of that?

He goes to take her in his arms, but she pushes him away.

Stella: Have I got to do it twice?

Syd: Well, you see . . .

Stella: *Have* I?

Syd: Well, yes. You see, I tried to make it only one show a night, but he wouldn't hear of it. He says it's absolutely essential you should do the supper turn. And you can see his point. I mean, after all, for double the money, it's worth it.

There is a momentary pause. Then she stands up.

Stella: No.

Syd: Now, darling . . .

Stella: No.

Suddenly she flings herself on the bed in a storm of tears. He sits down beside her on the bed and touches her shoulder helplessly.

Stella: I can't, Syd. I can't.

He tries to raise her.

Syd: Now, come on, darling, buck up. We can't turn down an offer like that. It means over four hundred pounds. With that extra we can be in business next year and forget all this. After all, it's not for long now.

She shakes her head.

Stella: No, I'm frightened. I don't want to die, Syd. I love you.

Syd: I know you do, darling, and I love you. Why, since we've been married I've never looked at another woman. But we've never had money like this before and we shan't again. You know what these things are. We're a riot now, but we can't expect it to go on forever. We've got to cash in.

Stella: Don't you mind if I die, Syd?

Syd: Don't talk so silly. Why, what should I be without you? You mustn't give way like this. You've got your self-respect to think of. You're famous.

Stella (*angrily*): Yes—like the Human Cannon Ball.

Syd: Now, Stella.

STELLA: That was an eye-opener to me. What do they come and see me over and over again for? On the chance they'll see me kill myself. And a week after I'm dead they'll have even forgotten my name. That's what the public is. When I looked at that old woman tonight I saw it all. (*She raises herself miserably.*) It's no good, Syd. I can't go on, I can't.

SYD: But I told you what Paco said. It's the supper trade. And, after all, if you can do it once . . .

STELLA: No. I can't do it again. (*She looks up at him.*) I mean *ever*, Syd.

He looks at her, his face hardening.

STELLA: Syd, dear, don't think I'm being silly. It's not just today. It's been growing on me. I can't sleep at night thinking of it. And when I do drop off, I see myself standing at the top of the ladder looking down. Tonight I could hardly get up there I was trembling so, and when you lit the flames . . . Syd, if you really loved me you wouldn't want me to go through such torture.

For a moment there is only the sound of her crying. Then he gets up slowly and goes over to the window. For a second or two he stands there trying to grapple with the situation. Then he goes round the beds to a suitcase and unlocks it with a key on a bunch from his pocket. From under some clothes in the suitcase he takes a thick tooled-leather wallet. Then he sits down on his bed and takes a bundle of bank notes out of the wallet. They are pinned together in small wads. He shuffles through them. He speaks tonelessly.

SYD: Three hundred thousand francs and a hundred and fifty odd dollars. That's what we've saved. Nearly enough. (*He puts it back in the wallet.*) It seems a pity to throw it all away.

STELLA (*brokenly*): I'm sorry, Syd.

SYD (*replacing the wallet*): Well, it can't be helped. I'll see Paco tomorrow and tell him. (*He looks across at her.*) I should get some rest if I were you, dear.

He picks up his jacket and puts it on. Her eyes, as she looks across from the bed, meet his.

SYD: I think I'll go for a bit of a walk.

On her face as wretchedly she watches him go . . .

41. *Exterior Monte Carlo. Day. A long shot of great beauty.*

42. *Exterior beach. Day. Some French children in swimming trunks run past shouting happily. The camera pans with them and on to Stella lying on a bathing wrap in the shade of an umbrella. For a moment she watches the children, then a shadow falls across her and she looks up. Syd sits down on the sand beside her. He is in jeans and a loose unbuttoned summer shirt. He does not look at her but at the sand which he sifts through his fingers.*

STELLA: Did you see Paco?

SYD: He wasn't there. He went into Nice just before lunch. He won't be back till this evening.

A pause.

STELLA: What will he do?

SYD: Well, I suppose he could sue us for breach of contract, or insist on a medical examination. We've still a few days to go on the old one, you know. But I doubt if it'd be worth his while. What he can do is see that we never get another job of any sort down here.

STELLA: Where shall we go then?

SYD (*shrugging*): I don't know. I haven't thought.

STELLA: Well, we have got some money.

SYD: Enough for six months, yes. Then it'll be the old life again.

STELLA: I know you think I'm unreasonable, Syd.

He smiles at her.

SYD: No, I don't, darling. . . .

He looks away. An almost dreamy note of longing comes into his voice as he goes on.

SYD: But just for a while I'd thought that one day we might be able to get out of this whole filthy business and live like human beings. Not to make a fortune I don't mean, but just to have something behind us, something steady. (*His voice gets bitter.*) We're not clever people. We're not in a profession that matters to us. Nobody cares if we go down the drain. We're a stunt. The only chance we ever had was to make our money quick, and save it, and buy ourselves out. (*He lies back on the sand.*) You don't want to take any notice of me. I'm just sorry for myself. I'll be all right and then we can make plans. Maybe we could go to Italy.

Stella is deeply troubled. There is a kind of desperation growing in her.

STELLA (*vaguely*): Or Spain?

SYD: No, no money in Spain.

She opens her eyes and looks at him. He is unaware of her. Slowly she sits up. She has made up her mind about something.

STELLA: I think I'll go along to the dressing room, Syd. I've some things to do.

SYD (*eyes shut*): Packing up before the blow falls, eh? Do you want any help?

STELLA (*quickly*): No, Syd. I can manage. You stay here and have a sleep.

SYD: O.K. Want to leave the cigarettes?

She puts an opened packet of French cigarettes into his hand and gets up. She looks down at him.

STELLA: Good-bye, Syd.

SYD: Bye-bye. Will you come back here?

As she picks up her beach wrap and moves away . . .

STELLA: Yes, all right.

DISSOLVE

43. *Interior hotel bedroom. Day. The shutters are closed against the brilliant sunshine. There are stripes of sunlight on the floor. Stella enters, shuts the door behind her, throws her beach wrap on the bed and goes over to the writing table. From the drawer in it she takes a bunch of keys. She selects a key, then, going to the suitcase in which Syd keeps their money, she unlocks and opens it. From its hiding place under the clothes in the suitcase, she takes the wallet of money. She looks at it for a moment, hesitates, then, making up her mind, relocks the suitcase. She is nervous and hurried now. She puts the keys and wallet down on the bed beside the beach wrap. She is wearing a beach skirt over her swimming suit. Quickly now she puts on the thin top jacket belonging to her skirt and, picking up the wallet, she goes out leaving the keys on the bed.*

44. *Exterior Monte Carlo Casino. Day. (Location.) Long shot of Monte Carlo Casino.*

45. *Exterior Monte Carlo Casino. Day. (Location.) Stella (double) hurries towards the Casino.*

46. *Insert. The roulette wheel spins. The ball is thrown in and rolls for a moment or two. As it begins clattering against the indentations of the wheel . . .*

47. *Interior Casino caisse. Day. Shooting over the hands of the Caissier on to Stella. He lets a neat pile of thousand-franc plaques clatter through his fingers onto the ledge of his booth. Stella puts the wallet away in her bag and, picking up the plaques, turns away.*

48. *Interior Casino. Roulette table. Day. Long shot. Stella moves into picture. A croupier spins the wheel.*
CROUPIER: *Faites vos jeux.*
The ball is thrown in.

49. *Interior Casino. Roulette table. Day. Medium close shot of Stella looking lost and bewildered. She makes up her mind and the camera tracks with her as she moves round the table.*
CROUPIER: *Rien ne va plus.*
The ball comes to rest.
CROUPIER: *Numéro sept . . . rouge, impair et manqué.*
Most of the stakes are raked in by the croupier. Some small wins are paid out. As this process goes on the rest of the scene is revealed.
Of those sitting and standing round the table, more than half are obviously holidaymakers. The rest are regulars. Of these, rather more are women than men. They occupy most of the seats round the table. Compared with the holiday gamblers, they are neatly dressed and somewhat dowdy-looking, though there are touches of eccentricity

about some of them. For example, the old lady in an Ed-
wardian lace tea gown and a rather large hat; a wizened
man who makes endless calculations in a notebook. The
holidaymakers are not important; they belong really to the
hot sunshine that can be seen through the tall windows of
the room. It is the serious players who matter, and they
are in the foreground, concentrating on the wheel, making
notes, choosing their moment to play, oblivious of the peo-
ple behind them.

Stella comes to a standstill. She stands behind a seated
woman whose face is concealed by a flamboyant hat, and
an old man with a shock of white hair. She leans forward
to put a stake of two plaques on the table.

STELLA: *Zéro et quatre premiers.*

A croupier nods and pushes the plaques into position.
Other stakes are going down.

50. *Interior Casino. Roulette table. Day. Close shot over*
the croupier's shoulder onto the wheel as he spins it.

CROUPIER: *Faites vos jeux.*

The ball is thrown in.

CROUPIER: *Rien ne va plus.*

51. *Interior Casino. Roulette table. Day. Stella anxiously*
watches the table.

52. *Interior Casino. Roulette table. Day. Close shot of the*
spinning roulette wheel, the ball clattering. The ball comes
to rest.

53. *Interior Casino. Roulette table. Day. Medium shot of*
the group, Stella watching anxiously.

CROUPIER: *Numéro deux . . . noir, pair et manque.*

Stella smiles. The croupier pushes eight plaques across
to her with his rake. As Stella leans forward to pick up the
plaques, the woman with the flamboyant hat below her
speaks.

WOMAN: *C'est assez curieux, vous savez . . .*

She breaks off as she recognizes Stella. She looks up. It
is Flora.

FLORA: Why, hullo, dear.

STELLA: Hullo.

FLORA: I was just going to say I've been playing on

quatre premiers all the afternoon and that's the first time it's come up. (*She sees the stack of plaques in Stella's hands.*) Here, come on. Have my seat.

STELLA: Thank you.

Stella takes Flora's seat at the table. Flora stands behind her.

FLORA: This is the first time I've seen you in here.

STELLA: Yes.

She puts her stake onto the table.

CROUPIER (*off*): *Faites vos jeux . . . rien ne va plus.*

There is the sound of the ball clattering into the wheel. Flora and Stella watch.

CROUPIER (*off*): *Numéro trente-six . . . rouge, pair et passe.*

FLORA: You know, I come here every day.

On a shot of the table with the croupiers raking in the stakes we . . .

DISSOLVE

54. *Exterior beach. Day. Syd, lying on the beach, opens his eyes. He is aware of sounds. A Frenchwoman is gathering her family together to leave the beach.*

FRENCHWOMAN: *Viens, Juliette. Viens, Claude. Vite, vite! On est déjà en retard. Vite, alors! Claude! Viens.*

Syd looks at his wrist watch. He gets up and slowly looks to see if Stella is coming.

DISSOLVE

55. *Interior Casino. Roulette table. Day. The croupier rakes in the stakes. Stella sits at the table with Flora behind her. Stella's face is set. Flora looks troubled. There is only one plaque on the table in front of Stella. She looks at it, then takes the wallet from her bag and takes out all the money left in it. As she does so Flora makes a movement to stop her.*

DISSOLVE

56. *Interior hotel bedroom. Day. Syd comes into the room as if expecting to see Stella. He looks round, then goes to the window, opens the shutters, and looks down into the street. He turns back into the room. The light from the*

late afternoon sun shines on the bed. In the light of the sun are the bunch of keys and Stella's beach wrap. Syd seizes the keys, quickly unlocks the suitcase and searches for the wallet. When he realizes that it has gone, he stands up slowly. He looks at the beach wrap, then turns and goes quickly out of the room.

57. *Interior Casino. Roulette table. Day. Shooting across the table. Stella sits staring desperately at the table.*

CROUPIER (*off*): *Rien ne va plus.*

There is the sound of the ball clattering in the wheel. Flora stands behind Stella looking worried.

CROUPIER (*off*): *Le numéro vingt-trois . . . rouge, impair et passe.*

58. *Interior Casino. Roulette table. Day. Shooting on to the croupiers, showing most of the table. The stakes are raked in by the Croupiers.*

59. *Interior Casino. Roulette table. Day. Medium close shot of Stella. She sits for a moment staring at the wheel. Then she looks down at the table in front of her. There is only the empty wallet.*

CROUPIER (*off*): *Faites vos jeux.*

Stella moves a step or two away. Flora puts her arm round her.

FLORA (*over—gently*): Never mind, dear. We all have our ups and downs.

60. *Interior Casino. Roulette table. Day. Two shot of Stella and Flora. Stella moves another step away.*

FLORA: What you need is a little something to drink. (*She puts the wallet in Stella's hand.*) Here, this is yours.

Stella looks down at the wallet.

STELLA: It was his money, not mine.

FLORA: Your husband's? Well, I expect you'll pay it back, dear. Maybe it's because it's Thursday. That table's always bad on Thursday.

DISSOLVE

61. *Exterior Casino Municipal. Day. Long shot of the entrance and steps of the Casino at Monte Carlo. Stella*

(double) and Flora (double) come out of the entrance to-
wards camera. In her hand Stella carries the wallet.

62. *Exterior Casino Municipal. Day. Close shot of Stella.*
She stops, looking across the square.

63. *Location. Syd (double) hurries across the Place du*
Casino. (N.B. This has already been shot.)

63a. *Exterior Casino Municipal. Day. Over Stella's shoulder.*
Syd stops at the foot of the steps. Stella stands looking at
him. He runs up the steps towards her and then, as she
makes no move towards him, he stops a yard or two from
her. He looks from the wallet to her face. He understands.
His mouth tightens.
SYD: Has it all gone? *(Bitterly)* You fool!
He turns and goes away down the steps.

64. *Exterior Casino Municipal. Day. Transparency close*
shot of Flora at the top of the steps, watching this scene.

65. *Exterior Casino Municipal. Day. Transparency shoot-*
ing down the steps. Stella takes another step after him. She
gives an almost inarticulate cry.
STELLA: Syd!
He does not hear her.

65a. *Location. Long shot. Place du Casino. As Syd*
(double) walks away, Stella runs down the steps of the
Casino and across the Place. (N.B. This has been shot.)

DISSOLVE

66. *Exterior Ritz Hotel terrace. Night. The place is*
crowded as usual. The orchestra is playing. People are
dancing.

67. *Interior Ritz Hotel bar. Night. The bar is crowded.*
Sandy Westcott makes his way to a table near the bar.
With him is the countess. The second barman comes up
to take their order. Paco comes by.
PACO: Good evening. Good evening, Countess.
COUNTESS: Hullo.
Paco moves out of shot and makes his way to the bar.
COUNTESS: You know, before Paco Espinel lost his
money he used to be quite attractive.

146

68. *Interior Ritz Hotel bar. Night. Shooting from behind the bar. At the bar, Paco beckons to the barman, who responds quickly.*

PACO: Has Mr. Cotman been in here?

BARMAN: I haven't seen him at all this evening, sir.

PACO: Are you sure?

BARMAN: Quite, sir.

PACO (*going*): Well, if he comes here, tell him I want to see him in my office.

DISSOLVE

69. *Interior Ritz Hotel passage and dressing room. Night. Shooting on to Paco's back, camera tracks with him as he goes through the swing doors and walks to the dressing-room door. Outside the dressing-room door stands Carlo. He is waiting. Paco glances at him as he knocks on the door. Carlo twirls his moustache. The dressing-room door is opened promptly by Flora.*

PACO (*frowning*): Is Mr. Cotman there?

FLORA: No, he isn't.

As Flora half closes the door . . .

70. *Interior Ritz Hotel passage and dressing room. Night. Stella has heard the conversation and hurries to open the door wider. She is in her dressing gown. She looks tired and hopeless.*

STELLA (*as she moves*): Oh, Mr. Espinel.

Paco Espinel moves into the dressing room.

PACO: Good evening, Mrs. Cotman. I was looking for your husband. He doesn't seem to be anywhere about, and its important that I see him.

STELLA: He won't be here.

She turns away.

PACO: What do you mean, he won't be here? He was supposed to bring me in your new contract. I've got to get the new posters out and the printer's waiting in my office for instructions. Is the contract signed?

STELLA (*wearily*): No, it isn't.

She sits down at her dressing table.

FLORA: What's the good of worrying her? Can't you see she's upset?

PACO: And who are you, madam?

FLORA: I'm a friend of hers.

PACO: Well, I must ask you to excuse us. (*To Stella*) I don't understand what's going on. Your husband agreed the terms on your behalf. Are you now refusing them?

STELLA: No, I'm not refusing.

FLORA: Now, dear, don't be silly. (*To Paco*) Can't you see? They've had a row. She can't go on and do that show.

PACO: She must go on. Last night at supper there were complaints.

FLORA (*to Stella*): Don't take any notice of him. You can't do that show, dear, and you know it. It's madness.

PACO (*to Flora*): I should be glad if you would get out of here.

FLORA: Anyway, how's she going to do it without him? Tell me that. She'll kill herself.

PACO (*angrily*): There is no risk. She does it night after night. She is used to it. Please get out and do not interfere.

Stella rises to her feet.

STELLA: Yes . . . it's time I was getting ready.

FLORA: But you're not going to do it tonight?

STELLA (*firmly*): Yes, I am. Tonight and every night. The band leader can make the announcements. And I'll tell them when to light the tank.

PACO: Good. I'll tell him. (*To Flora*) You see!

He goes out quickly. Flora still stands there pathetically.

FLORA: You can't, dear. You can't.

STELLA: Yes, I can. Tonight and every night. Until I kill myself.

She slips out of her dressing gown and stands looking at herself in the long mirror. She gives her reflection a hard smile.

STELLA: I mustn't disappoint my public.

Flora turns and goes quickly from the room.

DISSOLVE

71. *Interior hotel bedroom. Night. Syd is packing. But his movements are listless. After a moment or two he abandons the task and, flinging himself on the bed, stares at the ceiling. There is a tap at his door. Syd turns his head.*

SYD: *Qui est là?*

FLORA (*off*): It's me. . . .

Syd rolls off his bed and opens the door. Flora and Carlo are standing there. Syd stares at them, puzzled.

FLORA: . . . me and Carlo.

Carlo frowns.

CARLO: Good evening.

SYD: Good evening.

FLORA: May we come in?

SYD: Sure, if you want to.

They come in. There is an awkward pause.

SYD: Well?

FLORA: I was with your wife this afternoon.

SYD: Oh?

He picks a cigarette out of a packet and lights it.

FLORA: She did it for you, you know.

SYD: Don't you think you ought to mind your own business?

FLORA: I've never been a one for that, have I, Carlo?

CARLO: No, my dear.

Syd eyes them unkindly and sits on the bed.

FLORA: You see, she just wanted you to love her, that's all.

SYD: Excuse my saying so, but do you know what you're talking about?

CARLO (*indignant*): Now, please . . .

FLORA: All right, Carlo. (*To Syd*) All I'm telling you, me lad, is that if you don't do something quick you'll lose her. That's all.

SYD: What are you getting at?

FLORA: She'll kill herself if she does that dive tonight.

SYD: Well, if that's all you're worrying about, you can forget it. She's not doing the dive any more. She's lost her nerve. And if you don't mind my saying so, it was all that talk of yours last night that did it.

FLORA: If you believe that, me lad, you're an even bigger fool than I took you for. She lost her nerve because she's come to think that it's the cash that matters to you, not her.

Syd leaps to his feet.

SYD: The cash! What do you mean, the cash? What do you take me for? I love Stella and I don't care who knows it. I wouldn't let her make that dive again for all the money in the place.

FLORA: That's not what she thinks, and if you don't

149

believe me you'd better get along there now before she does put on a show for them.

SYD: Ah, you're crazy. Besides, she can't do the show without me.

FLORA (*brutally*): Can't she? "I mustn't disappoint my public," she said. "The band leader can make the announcements."

For a moment Syd stares at them in horror. Then, suddenly, he rushes to the door, flings it open and dashes out of the room.

72. *Exterior Ritz Hotel terrace. Night. Close shot of the drummer. There is a roll of drums.*

73. *Exterior Ritz Hotel terrace. Night. Long shot, over the drummer's shoulder. The spotlights are on the ladder and tank. The roll of drums comes to an end. The dancers are leaving the floor to return to their tables.*

74. *Exterior Ritz Hotel terrace. Night. Shooting on to Sandy Westcott's table. Sandy Westcott and the Countess are at a table near the tank. They are joined by Eva Barrett and the Prince.*

EVA BARRETT: Sergei thinks I'm out of my mind.

PRINCE (*tolerantly*): I tell her it's a fake, but she insists upon coming.

SANDY: For the trout and the roast chicken?

EVA BARRETT: I'm simply starving.

We hear another roll of drums.

75. *Exterior Monte Carlo street. Night. Syd runs breathlessly along the street. As he comes to a corner, there is the sound of a car.*

76. *Exterior Monte Carlo street. Night. He looks round, pauses and desperately signals to the car as it drives by. The car does not stop. Syd turns aside and runs on down a steep alleyway of steps.*

77. *Interior Ritz Hotel passage and dressing room. Night. An attendant is knocking on the dressing-room door.*

ATTENDANT (*calling*): *Madame Stella! Vite! On vous attend!*

The door opens and Stella comes out of the dressing

*room. Her face is quite immobile. She is sick with fear.
Paco comes through the swing doors to meet her. The
camera tracks back with them as they move up the passage.*

PACO: Are you all right? I thought something had happened.

STELLA: (*dully*): Syd usually calls me. Does the band
leader understand?

PACO: When you say ready, he lights the tank.

STELLA: Yes.

*Paco holds the swing door for her. He sees that all is not
well with her.*

PACO: You *are* all right, aren't you?

STELLA: Would an accident be bad for business?

PACO (*smiling feebly*): Ah, you're joking, my dear.

He follows her anxiously through the door.

78. *Exterior Ritz Hotel terrace. Night. The roll of drums
ends. The band leader steps to the middle of the floor into
the spotlights. He addresses the audience with a strong
foreign accent.*

BAND LEADER: Ladies and gentlemen. You are now going
to see the most marvellous feat of the century . . .

79. *Exterior Ritz Hotel terrace. Night. Shooting on to Eva
Barrett's table. The band leader's voice continues behind
their conversation.*

SANDY: I say, what's happened to Cotman?

EVA BARRETT: Who's Cotman?

SANDY: Her husband—the one who usually makes the
announcements. I wonder what's happened.

COUNTESS: Does it matter? *She* does the dive.

SANDY: Yes, but . . .

BAND LEADER (*concluding*): Ladies and gentlemen. I
have the honour to present Madame Stella.

Sandy looks at the floor.

80. *Exterior Ritz Hotel terrace. Night. Long shot. Stella
runs from the side into the glare of the lights. She bows
to the audience as before, but she does not smile.*

81. *Exterior Ritz Hotel terrace. Night. Shooting on to
Eva Barrett's table. Sandy Westcott is watching keenly.*

SANDY: I think there's something up.

PRINCE: Perhaps her husband has gone off with the tattooed lady.

SANDY (*watching*): There *is* something up.

82. *Ritz Hotel terrace. Night. Shooting from the foot of the ladder. Stella finishes her bow and walks towards the foot of the ladder. The lights follow her as before. She steps out of her dressing gown and the band leader takes it. She goes to the foot of the ladder and as she looks up . . .*

83. *Exterior Ritz Hotel terrace. Night. Shooting up the ladder from Stella's eyeline. There is a pause as she hesitates, then her head moves into shot and she starts to climb.*

84. *Exterior Place du Casino. Night. Syd turns a corner and runs frantically across the Place in the direction of the Sporting Club.*

85. *Exterior Ritz Hotel terrace. Night. Crane shot. Shooting down the ladder as Stella is climbing slowly. Her breathing is very quick and shallow. The voice of the band leader can be heard from below.*

BAND LEADER: . . . I must therefore ask you, when the word is given, to remain absolutely still and silent. Thank you, mesdames et messieurs . . .

As he continues in French, Stella pauses and leans against the ladder. She looks down. Pull focus to sharpen the terrace beneath.

BAND LEADER: . . . *cet étonnant tour de force ne pout réussir que par la suprême habileté et l'exact jugement de Madame Stella. Il exige un recueillement absolu. Le moindre bruit peut être fatal. Je dois donc, lorsque je vous donnerai le signal, vous prier de vous tenir absolument immobiles et de garder le plus profond silence.*

86. *Interior Ritz Hotel passage and dressing room. Night. Syd dashes along the passage and flings open the dressing-room door. The room is empty.*

87. *Exterior Ritz Hotel terrace. Night. Shooting through the ladder on to Stella as she climbs into picture. Tears are running down her cheeks and she stops.*

88. *Exterior Ritz Hotel terrace. Night. Shooting on to Eva Barrett's table. The band leader (off) is continuing the*

French announcement (as in Scene 85.) All are looking up.
   SANDY: She's stopped. What's the matter with her?
   PRINCE (*disdainfully*): No, she's going on.

89. *Exterior Ritz Hotel terrace. Night. Medium long shot on to Stella's back as she climbs again up and out of picture.*

90. *Exterior Ritz Hotel terrace. Night. Shooting on to the service entrance to the terrace. An attendant tries to stop Syd from getting in. Syd thrusts the man out of the way and is going on when Paco stops him, seizing his arm.*
   PACO: Cotman, where have you been?
   SYD: Espinel, Stella can't do that dive tonight.
   He breaks away from Paco.
   PACO: What are you talking about?
   He hastens after Syd.

91. *Exterior Ritz Hotel terrace. Night. Medium shot. Stella reaches her diving platform and climbs onto it.*

92. *Exterior Ritz Hotel terrace. Night. Long shot, over Stella's shoulder, of the whole terrace.*

93. *Exterior Ritz Hotel terrace. Night. Tracking shot. Paco grabs Syd's arm as he pushes his way between the tables.*
   PACO: Are you mad?
   SYD: Do you want her to kill herself?
   PACO: She is all right. She said she was all right.
   SYD: She isn't all right. If you won't stop it, I will!
   Syd's voice has risen. As they pass Eva Barrett's table, they go out of picture and the camera holds on the table. Syd's voice has attracted Sandy's attention.
   SANDY: Hullo, hullo. Look at our Mr. Cotman. There's something the matter.
   The roll of drums begins. All look up.

94. *Exterior Ritz Hotel terrace. Night. Very long shot of Stella from their eyeline. (Matte.)*

95. *Exterior Ritz Hotel terrace. Night. Very close shot of Stella as she steps forward to the edge of her platform. She looks down.*

96. *Exterior Ritz Hotel terrace. Night. From Stella's eyeline. The terrace below begins to revolve. A spinning*

roulette wheel is superimposed on the mouth of the tank. The scene begins to tilt.

97. *Exterior Ritz Hotel terrace. Night. Full-length shot of Stella. She shuts her eyes. She begins to sway on her feet.*

98. *Exterior Ritz Hotel terrace. Night. Shooting on to Eva Barrett's table. Everyone is looking up.*
    SANDY: She's going to fall.
    A waiter pouring wine looks up. The wine runs over the table.

99. *Exterior Ritz Hotel terrace. Night. Shooting through the ladder. Syd pushes his way frantically between the tables.*
    SYD (*shouting*): Stella! Stella!
    He makes for the foot of the ladder. Waiters try to stop him. He pushes them aside and runs to the ladder.
    SYD (*shouting*): Stella! Come back!

100. *Exterior Ritz Hotel terrace. Night. Medium shot of Stella. She puts her hand up to her head—she seems about to faint. Syd's voice comes very faintly to her.*
    SYD (*off*): Stella, darling!

101. *Exterior Ritz Hotel terrace. Night. Shooting from Stella's eyeline from the top of the ladder. Syd starts to climb swiftly towards her.*
    SYD: Stella!

102. *Exterior Ritz Hotel terrace. Night. Very close shot of Stella. She opens her eyes.*

103. *Exterior Ritz Hotel terrace. Night. Blurred eyeline shot from Stella's viewpoint. The terrace beneath her swirls.*
    SYD (*off*): Come back, darling!
    The terrace from her viewpoint suddenly becomes clear and steady. Syd comes up the ladder towards her.

104. *Exterior Ritz Hotel terrace. Night. Crane shot. From Syd's eyeline, moving slowly up towards her.*

105. *Exterior Ritz Hotel terrace. Night. Shooting down past Stella's legs, on to Syd as he climbs up towards her.*

106. *Exterior Ritz Hotel terrace. Night. Close shot of Stella. Suddenly her face clears. Tremulously she smiles.*
STELLA: Hullo, Syd.

107. *Exterior Ritz Hotel terrace. Night. Close shot of Syd as he pauses.*
SYD: Hold on, darling.

108. *Exterior Ritz Hotel Terrace. Night. Longer shot. Syd climbs a few more steps.*
STELLA: I just felt a bit faint.
SYD: Nothing else matters but us. Hold on.
She smiles and turns to face outwards, ready for a dive.
STELLA (*calling out*): Ready!
In a panic Syd turns and looks down.

109. *Exterior Ritz Hotel terrace. Night. Long shot of the tank from Syd's eyeline. An attendant approaches the tank with a torch.*

110. *Exterior Ritz Hotel terrace. Night. Close shot of the tank as the torch lights the petrol and flames shoot up.*

111. *Exterior Ritz Hotel terrace. Night. Two shot over Syd's shoulder bottom of frame on to Stella.*
SYD: Stella!
She smiles down at him over her shoulder. She is sure of herself now.
STELLA (*quietly*): I'm all right now.
She braces herself for a dive.

112. *Exterior hotel terrace. Night. Long shot over Stella's shoulder down onto the terrace and burning tank. She is poised for a second, very still.*

113. *Exterior Ritz Hotel terrace. Night. Cut back to the two shot, with Syd in bottom of frame as she dives past camera.*
SYD (*off*): Stella!
Close shot of Stella as she moves into dive, camera tracking in.
SYD (*off*): Stella!

114. *Exterior Ritz Hotel terrace. Night. Shooting down, the terrace and burning tank from Stella's eyeline. She*

dives, but this time the camera gives us the impression that we are hurtling down with her towards the flames. As we strike them—slow dissolve. Through the end music we hear the applause of the restaurant audience. We know Stella is safe.

FADE OUT

THE END